HIGHER
GCSE Modular Mathematics
for Edexcel

HOMEWORK BOOK

JEAN LINSKY

SERIES EDITOR: ALAN SMITH

Hodder Murray

A MEMBER OF THE HODDER HEADLINE GROUP

Acknowledgements

This high quality material is endorsed by Edexcel and has been through a rigorous quality assurance programme to ensure that it is a suitable companion to the specification for both learners and teachers. This does not mean that its contents will be used verbatim when setting examinations nor is it to be read as being the official specification – a copy of which is available at www.edexcel.org.uk

Hodder Headline's policy is to use papers that are natural, renewable and recyclable products and made from wood grown in sustainable forests. The logging and manufacturing processes are expected to conform to the environmental regulations of the country of origin.

Orders: please contact Bookpoint Ltd, 130 Milton Park, Abingdon, Oxon OX14 4SB. Telephone: (44) 01235 827720. Fax: (44) 01235 400454. Lines are open 9.00 – 5.00, Monday to Saturday, with a 24-hour message answering service. Visit our website at www.hoddereducation.co.uk

© Jean Linsky and Alan Smith 2007
First published in 2007 by
Hodder Murray, an imprint of Hodder Education,
a member of the Hodder Headline Group,
an Hachette Livre UK Company,
338 Euston Road
London NW1 3BH

Impression number   5   4   3   2   1
Year   2012   2011   2010   2009   2008   2007

Cover photo © David Angel @ Début Art
Illustrations © Barking Dog Art
Typeset in 10 point Times Ten Roman by Tech Set Ltd
Printed in Great Britain by Martins of Berwick

A catalogue record for this title is available from the British Library

ISBN: 978 0 340 95916 9

Contents

Introduction

This Homework Book has been written to support the Hodder Murray Student's Books for the two-tier Edexcel GCSE Modular Mathematics (Higher Tier) specification and takes into account the withdrawal of coursework from GCSE Mathematics.

The sequence of the material mirrors that of the Student's Books, so that, for example, Exercise 7.2 of the Homework Book provides further practice questions matching the content of Exercise 7.2 in the Student's Book (see table below for details of Unit renumbering).

In Unit 1 (Data Handling), Chapters 1–4 contain a blend of Foundation and Higher material and students taking the Higher Tier should do exercises marked **H**. Chapters 5 and 6 are Higher Tier only.

In Unit 2, Stage 1 Exercises are marked with and Stage 2 Exercises are marked with

More practice helps to reinforce the ideas you have learned and makes it easier to remember at a later stage. If, however, you do forget, further help is at hand. As well as the Student's Books, with this book there is also a Personal Tutor CD-ROM. This contains worked examples on key topics to help you recall what you may have forgotten.

Look out for this symbol **pt** next to an exercise; it tells you that there is a relevant worked example on the CD-ROM.

For all the questions in this book, an icon shows you whether calculators are permitted or not, and you should follow this advice carefully in order to build up the necessary mixture of calculator and non-calculator skills before the examination.

All of the content of this book has been checked very carefully against the new GCSE specification, to ensure that all examination topics are suitably covered. In addition, practice exam-style papers, with full mark schemes, are available in Hodder Murray's accompanying Assessment Pack.

The table below indicates how the units have been renumbered following the withdrawal of coursework; the shaded column corresponds to the units in this book.

Specification (Modular) with coursework	Specification (Modular) without coursework
First examination March 2007 and first certification June 2008	First examination March 2008 and first certification June 2009
Unit 1: Internal coursework assessment	No coursework assessment
Unit 2: Handling data	**Unit 1:** Handling data
Unit 3: Number and algebra/Shape, space and measures 1	**Unit 2: Stage 1** (non-calculator multiple choice paper) + **Stage 2** (calculator paper): Number and algebra/Shape, space and measures 1
Unit 4: Number and algebra/Shape, space and measures 2	**Unit 3:** Number and algebra/Shape, space and measures 2

UNIT 1

U1 CHAPTER 1

Collecting data

EXERCISE 1.1   H

1 Fran carries out a survey.
She wants to see whether the school canteen should be open every day.
She decides to arrive at the canteen at 12 noon and ask the first 50 students who arrive the question:

'Don't you agree that our school canteen should stay open every day?'

a) Write down **two** reasons why this is **not** a good way to find out whether students at Fran's school think the school canteen should be open every day.
b) Describe a better method of selecting 50 students that Fran might use.
c) Write down a replacement question that Fran could use.

2 Keith is conducting a survey about restaurants in his town.
Here are three questions in his questionnaire.

1 How old are you?   _____

2 What restaurant do you go to?   _____

3 Do you agree that restaurants are too expensive?

YES ☐   NO ☐   (Tick one)

a) Explain briefly why each of Keith's questions is unsuitable.
b) Design suitable replacements for each of Keith's questions.

3 Sarah is going to find out about the make-up habits of the female students and teachers at her school.
She has designed three questions:

1 Are you (Please tick)   Student ☐   Teacher ☐

2 How old are you?

3 How much make-up do you use?

A lot ☐   Not very much ☐

a) Explain briefly why Sarah's questions 2 and 3 are unsuitable.
b) Design suitable replacements for questions 2 and 3 in Sarah's questionnaire.

4 Reeve wants to find out about the amount of pocket money students at her school get.
She has designed three questions.

1 Who gives you your pocket money?

2 Who is your favourite sports personality?

3 How much do you get?   £3–£5   £5–£7   £7 or more

a) Criticise each of Reeve's questions.
b) Design suitable replacements for questions 1 and 3 in Reeve's questionnaire.

5 Harry wants to collect information about how many calls students make on their mobile phones. Design a suitable question he could use on a questionnaire.

6 Ella wants to find out how much television students watch.

She uses this question on a questionnaire.

> How many hours of TV do you watch?
>
> ☐ 0–3   ☐ 3–6   ☐ 6–9   ☐ 9 or more

Write down two things wrong with this question.

EXERCISE 1.2

State whether the following sets of data would be categorical, discrete or continuous.

1 The number of cars in the school car park.

2 The shoe sizes of the people in your class.

3 The number of hours of television people watch each week.

4 The amount of water people drink in a day.

5 The weight of the contents in customers' shopping trolleys.

6 The heights of the dogs at a dog show.

7 The colours of people's clothes at a concert.

8 The amount waiters earn in tips at a restaurant.

9 The favourite chocolate bar of the students at your school.

10 The number of times a spinner lands on red.

11 The mark that the people in your class scored in a test.

12 The time students take to get to school.

13 The days of the week that people watch television.

14 The volume of water that people use in a bath.

15 The number of days people go abroad in a year.

EXERCISE 1.3

Do not use your calculator for Questions 1–4.

1   Kate carries out a survey about her friends' favourite pets.
    She makes a frequency table of her results.

Pet	Tally	Frequency
Cat	||||| ||||| |||||	15
Dog	||||| |||	8
Hamster	||||| |||||		
Goldfish	||||	
Birds	||	
Rabbit	||||| ||||| ||||| |||	

a)   Complete a copy of Kate's frequency table.
b)   How many people liked goldfish best?
c)   Which is the favourite pet of most of Kate's friends?
d)   Which is the least favourite pet of most of Kate's friends?
e)   How many friends did Kate ask altogether?

2   Anna collects data about the flavour of fruit drink people buy in the canteen.
    Here are her results.

lemon	mango	apple	lemon	orange	mango
apple	orange	orange	apple	mango	pear
apple	pear	mango	mango	lemon	apple
orange	mango	lemon	lemon	mango	mango
apple	mango	apple	apple	orange	mango

a)   Complete a copy of the frequency table to show Anna's results.

Flavour of drink	Tally	Frequency
apple		
lemon		
mango		
orange		
pear		

b)   Which flavour was the most popular?
c)   How many more people preferred apple to pear?
d)   Which two flavours were equally popular?

3 Lisa has carried out a survey to find out the marks students got in their last test.
Here are the marks for the students in her class.

45	55	73	28	87	67	49	52	57	40
20	57	47	92	78	45	61	25	70	42
52	43	41	22	74	74	45	33	62	51

a) Complete the frequency table to show Lisa's results.

Mark	Tally	Frequency
20 and under		
21–30		
31–40		
41–50		
51–60		
61–70		
71–80		
Over 80		

b) How many students got between 41 and 50 marks?
c) How many students scored more than 60 marks?
d) How many students were in Lisa's class?

4 The weights of 36 potatoes were recorded.
The results, in grams, are shown below.

127	163	242	280	339	207	200	97	151	262	190	73
333	310	230	250	222	80	150	328	200	111	102	273
208	212	217	143	349	285	146	174	285	243	291	187

a) Complete the frequency table to show these results.

Weight, w (in g)	Tally	Frequency
$0 < w \leqslant 100$		
$100 < w \leqslant 150$		
$150 < w \leqslant 200$		
$200 < w \leqslant 250$		
$250 < w \leqslant 300$		
$300 < w \leqslant 350$		

b) How many potatoes weighed 200 grams or less?

5 Will collected some data on the number of hours his friends spent on the computer on Sunday. Here are the times, correct to the nearest hour.

4	2	0	4	4	5	2	3	1	1	5	6
2	1	0	4	4	4	3	1	3	2	1	3

a) Copy and complete the frequency table.

Number of hours	Tally	Frequency
0		
1		
2		
3		
4		
5		
6		

b) How many of Will's friends spent 4 hours, to the nearest hour, on the computer?

c) How many of Will's friends spent more than 4 hours, to the nearest hour, on the computer?

d) How many hours did Will's friends spend on the computer in total?

EXERCISE 1.4 H

1 Jonathan has been carrying out a survey.
He asked some tea and coffee drinkers whether they drank tea or coffee or both.
Here are some of his results, transferred into a two-way table.

	Tea	Coffee	Both	Total
Male	15			42
Female		12	17	
Total			32	100

a) Copy and complete the two-way table.   **b)** How many females drank only tea?
c) How many men were in the survey?   **d)** How many people drank only coffee?

2 Jess asked 80 people to give their favourite colour from blue, green, red or yellow.
This two-way table shows some of her results.

	Blue	Green	Red	Yellow	Total
Boys			8	6	
Girls	7			2	36
Total	20		31		80

a) Copy and complete the two-way table.
b) How many people liked red best?
c) How many girls liked green best?
d) How many boys were asked?

3 Jean has collected data on how much weight (*w*), in kg, people at her slimming club have lost
over the last 6 months.
This two-way table shows some of her results.

		Men	Women	Total
	$0 < w \leqslant 5$	1		10
	$5 < w \leqslant 10$		26	
Weight in kg	$10 < w \leqslant 15$	‐	17	27
	over 15	9	11	
	Total	27		

a) Copy and complete the two-way table.
b) How many women lost more than 15 kg?
c) How many men lost more than 10 kg?
d) How many women lost 10 kg or less?
e) How many people took part in Jean's survey?

4 The two-way table shows the number of children and the number of pets in some families.

Number of children

		0	1	2	3 or more
Number of pets	0	4	4	3	1
	1	3	3	6	5
	2	2	3	4	2
	3 or more	5	1	0	0

a) How many families have 2 children and one pet?
b) How many families have 1 child and two pets?
c) How many families have 3 or more pets?
d) How many families have the same number of children as pets?
e) How many families took part in the survey?

5 The two-way table shows the number of cinemas and the number of large supermarkets in some small towns.

Number of supermarkets

		1	2	3	4
Number of cinemas	0	0	7	8	3
	1	2	8	6	4
	2	1	10	15	2
	3	0	6	7	1

a) How many small towns have 4 supermarkets and 2 cinemas?
b) How many small towns have exactly 1 supermarket?
c) How many small towns have the same number of supermarkets as cinemas?
d) How many small towns have fewer supermarkets than cinemas?

6 Mel is carrying out a survey to see whether teachers and students like the same music.
She asks each person in the sample to name their favourite type of music.
Mel records the results on a data collection sheet.
Here are her results after asking the first 14 people.

Pop	Classical	Jazz	Folk	Teachers	Students
卌 II	II	IIII	I	卌 I	卌 III

a) Explain one disadvantage with recording the data in this way.
b) Design an improved data collection sheet that Mel might use.

7 Design a data collection sheet for a survey about how much homework students get.

U1 CHAPTER 2

Working with statistics

EXERCISE 2.1

Do not use your calculator for Questions 1–3.

1 Find: **(i)** the mean, **(ii)** the median and **(iii)** the mode of the following sets of data.

a)	4	4	5	5	8	8	8		
b)	5	7	7	7	11	12	13	14	14
c)	10	10	11	13	16				

2 Pat surveys her friends to find out about their favourite colours.
Here are her results.

red	blue	green	blue	black
green	red	yellow	white	orange
pink	purple	brown	red	black

Which colour is the mode?

3 Mina surveys some students about their favourite subject at school.
Here are her results.

Subject	Frequency
Art	25
Drama	38
English	18
Mathematics	4
Science	2

Which subject is the mode?

You can use a calculator for Questions 4–7.

4 Find: **(i)** the mean, **(ii)** the median and **(iii)** the mode of the following sets of data.

a)	5	2	9	8	0	2	3	7	1	
b)	64	68	75	63	68	74	72	63	78	70	73
c)	125	136	128	130	130	129	120			

5 Find: **(i)** the mean, **(ii)** the median and **(iii)** the mode of the following sets of data.

a)	4	7	9	12	4	2	13	10	
b)	30	38	48	41	25	27	41	38	41	32
c)	43	35	50	31	37	43			

6 Jeremy wants to sell his business.
He puts an advertisement in the local paper.

> **BUSINESS FOR SALE**
> Average annual profit
> £80 000
> Telephone: 8488 5901

Here are his annual profits (to the nearest £10 000) for the past 15 years.

£200 000	£180 000	£150 000	£160 000	£170 000
£140 000	£90 000	£80 000	£60 000	£50 000
£50 000	£40 000	£50 000	£50 000	£30 000

   a) Find the mean profit.
   b) Find the median profit.
   c) Which average has the advertisement used?
      Is this a reasonable average to take?
      Give a reason for your answer.

7 Joe recorded the temperature at midnight for 12 nights during February.
Here are his results.

2 °C   −5 °C   −4 °C   0 °C   1 °C   −3 °C
−2 °C   1 °C   2 °C   1 °C   −2 °C   −5 °C

Find the:
   a) mean temperature   **b)** median temperature   **c)** modal temperature.

EXERCISE 2.2

 1. Find: **(i)** the mean, **(ii)** the median, **(iii)** the mode and **(iv)** the range of the following sets of data.

a)	3	7	3	7	7	1	1	7	6	2
b)	13	17	13	17	17	11	11	17	16	12
c)	73	77	73	77	77	71	71	77	76	72
d)	213	217	213	217	217	211	211	217	216	212

   e) What do you notice about your answers?

You can use a calculator for Questions 2 and 3.

2 The data set below gives the total number of marks scored by each of 21 students in a test.

67	54	39	63	54	70	43
60	50	64	38	61	87	68
42	55	66	80	33	41	35

   a) Work out the range of the data.
   b) Write down the mode.
   c) Calculate the value of the mean.
   d) Find the value of the median.

3 Here are the heights and the weights of 8 students.

Name	Sarah	Rose	Anna	Lisa	Mia	Alison	Jo	Pat
Height	1.5 m	1.27 m	1.42 m	1.67 m	1.27 m	1.4 m	1.61 m	1.56 m
Weight	78.2 kg	95 kg	73.7 kg	85 kg	62.1 kg	80.2 kg	85 kg	62 kg

a) For the heights, work out the:
  (i) mean   **(ii)** median   **(iii)** range.
b) For the weights, work out the:
  (i) mean   **(ii)** median   **(iii)** range.
c) Which person was not very tall but weighed a lot?

EXERCISE 2.3 H

1 A company sells beds in flat packs for customers to build.
This stem and leaf diagram shows the times, in minutes, it took for each of 14 people to build a bed.

```
2 | 4  5
3 | 3  8  8
4 | 0  1  7  9
5 | 2  5  6
6 | 1  7
```

Key: 2 | 4 = 24

Four more people build a bed from a flat pack.
Their times, in minutes, are 52, 48, 69 and 52.
a) Redraw the stem and leaf diagram and include the four new people.
Using your stem and leaf diagram:
b) Find the mode
c) Find the median
d) Find the range.

2 Patsy has made an unsorted stem and leaf diagram to show the weights, in grams, of 23 loaves of bread in her bakery.

```
70 | 6  4  1
71 | 7  4  0  6  7
72 | 3  9  5  4
73 | 9  8  5  8  3  8
74 | 6  6  4  9  0
```

Key: 70 | 6 = 706

a) Redraw the diagram so that it is fully ordered.
Using your stem and leaf diagram:
b) Find the mode
c) Find the median
d) Find the range.

3 There were 15 pairs of trainers in a sale.
Their prices, in £, are shown below:

23	38	29	53	46	40	23	37
20	34	56	42	33	39	21	

   a) Draw a stem and leaf diagram to show this information.
        Remember to include a key.
   b) Work out the range of the prices.
   c) Find the median price.

4 A cycling group went on a 13-day holiday.
Here are the number of kilometres they planned to cycle each day.

18	32	23	28	19	40	41
25	34	38	19	22	27	

   a) Draw a stem and leaf diagram to show this information.
        Remember to include a key.
   b) Work out the range.
   c) Find the median.

5 16 students sat an English examination.
Here are their marks:

72	68	53	60	72	50	83	57
50	75	81	76	65	69	60	71

   a) Draw a stem and leaf diagram to show this information.
   b) Find the median of the marks.

 EXERCISE 2.4 H

1 Alan is an estate agent.
He gathers some data on the number of apartments available in 100 large apartment blocks.

Number of apartments	Frequency
1	28
2	35
3	21
4	9
5	7
Total	100

   a) What is the modal number of apartments available?
   b) Find the median number of apartments available.
   c) Work out the mean number of apartments available.
   d) What is the range of Alan's data?

You can use a calculator for Questions 2 and 3.

2 Lilian conducts a survey.
She finds out how many hours of TV students watched last Monday.
The frequency table shows her results.

a) How many students took part in Lilian's survey?

The average number of hours of TV watched is 4.

Lilian

Number of hours watching TV	Frequency
0	2
1	7
2	9
3	4
4	3
5 or more	0
Total	

b) Explain why Lilian must be wrong.
c) Find the modal number of hours of TV watched.
d) Find the range of the data.
e) Work out the mean number of hours of TV watched.
f) Find the median number of hours of TV watched.

3 Jasmine is surveying the local hockey club.
She records the number of goals scored in each hockey match in the past three years.

a) How many matches did Jasmine survey?
b) What is the modal number of goals per match?
c) Find the median number of goals per match.
d) Work out the mean number of goals per match.
e) What is the range of Jasmine's data?

Number of goals	Frequency
0	3
1	2
2	5
3	7
4	2
5	3
6	0
7	0
8	1
Total	

EXERCISE 2.5 H

1 Hajra has measured the weights of some babies and toddlers at a crèche.
The frequency table shows her results.

Weight (w) in kg	Frequency (f)
$0 < w \leqslant 4$	5
$4 < w \leqslant 8$	6
$8 < w \leqslant 12$	7
$12 < w \leqslant 16$	2
$16 < w \leqslant 20$	1
Total	

   a) State the modal class.
   b) Find the class interval in which the median lies.
   c) Estimate the mean weight of these babies and toddlers.
   Show all your working clearly.

You can use a calculator for Questions 2–4.

2 Mario records the number of people at the gym each day in April.
The frequency table shows his results.

Number of people at the gym	Frequency	Midpoint
28 to 34	4	
35 to 41	8	
42 to 48	12	
49 to 55	6	
Total		

   a) Copy the table, and fill in the midpoint values in the third column.
   b) Use the table to help you calculate an estimate of the mean number of people at the gym each day in April.
   c) State the modal class.
   d) Find the class interval which contains the median.
   e) Carlo says, 'The range is 30.'
   Explain why Carlo must be wrong.

3 The frequency table shows the ages of the passengers on a cruise liner on the Atlantic.

a) State the modal class.
b) Find the class interval which contains the median.
c) Work out an estimate of the mean age of the passengers on the cruise liner. Give your answer correct to three significant figures.

Age (A) in years	Frequency
$0 < A \leqslant 20$	38
$20 < A \leqslant 40$	70
$40 < A \leqslant 60$	75
$60 < A \leqslant 80$	15
$80 < A \leqslant 100$	2
Total	

4 Seamus solves some Sudoku puzzles.
The frequency table shows the times taken to solve each puzzle.

Time (t) in minutes	Frequency
$5 \leqslant t < 10$	4
$10 \leqslant t < 15$	5
$15 \leqslant t < 20$	7
$20 \leqslant t < 25$	9
$25 \leqslant t < 30$	5
Total	

a) State the modal class.
b) Find the class interval which contains the median.
c) Calculate an estimate of the mean time Seamus took to solve the puzzles.
d) Explain briefly why your answer can only be an estimate.

 EXERCISE 2.6 H

1 Match together these graphs with their descriptions.

P   Q   R

A   Length of hair against Height
B   Value of car against Age of car
C   Height against Weight

2 A park has an outdoor swimming pool.
The scatter graph shows the maximum temperature and the number of people who used the pool on ten Saturdays in summer.

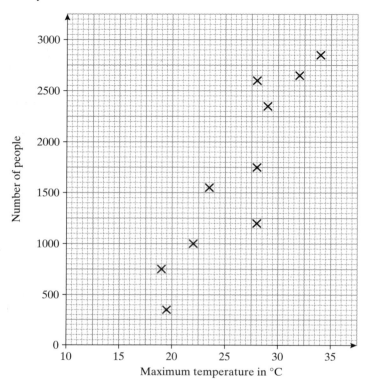

a) Describe the correlation between the maximum temperature and the number of people who used the pool.

b) On a copy of the scatter graph, draw a line of best fit.

The weather forecast for the next Saturday gives a maximum temperature of 27 °C.

c) Use your line of best fit to estimate the number of people who will use the pool.

[Edexcel]

3 Some students took a Mathematics test and a Science test.
The scatter graph shows information about the test marks of eight students.

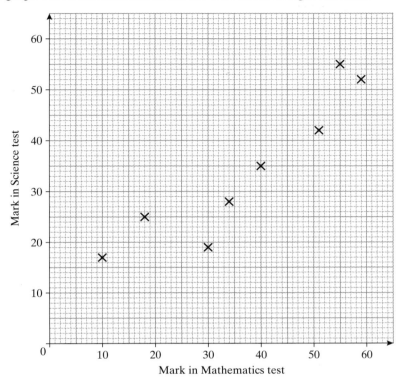

Mark in Mathematics test

The table shows the test marks of four more students.

Mark in Mathematics test	14	25	50	58
Mark in Science test	21	23	38	51

a) On a copy of the scatter graph, plot the information from the table.
b) Draw a line of best fit on the scatter graph.
c) Describe the **correlation** between the marks in the Mathematics test and the marks in the Science test.

[Edexcel]

4 Ten men took part in a long jump competition.
The table shows the heights of the ten men and the best jumps they made.

Best jump (m)	5.33	6.00	5.00	5.95	4.80	5.72	4.60	5.80	4.40	5.04
Height of men (m)	1.70	1.80	1.65	1.75	1.65	1.74	1.60	1.75	1.60	1.67

a) On a copy of the grid above plot the points as a scatter diagram.
b) Describe the relationship between the height and the maximum difference.
c) Draw in a line of best fit.

[Edexcel]

5 Here is a scatter graph.
One axis is labelled 'Height'.
a) For this graph, state the type
of correlation.
b) From the list below, choose the most appropriate
label for the other axis:

Length of hair
Number of sisters
Length of legs
GCSE French mark

[Edexcel]

6 The scatter graph shows information about twelve athletes.
It shows the time each athlete took to run 100 metres and the length of their best long jump.

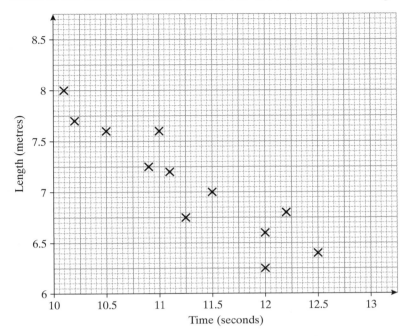

a) Describe the **correlation** between time taken to run 100 metres and length of best long jump.

b) Draw a line of best fit on the scatter graph.

7 a) Here are two scatter graphs, A and B.

For each scatter graph, select the words that best describe the correlation.

	Positive correlation	Negative correlation	No correlation
A			
B			

U1 CHAPTER 3

Presenting data

EXERCISE 3.1

1 Simone wrote down the favourite colours of all the students in her class.
The bar chart shows her results.

a) Which colour was the favourite for five of the students?

b) Which was the favourite colour?

c) Two colours were equally popular. Which colours were they?

d) How many students were in Simone's class?

2 A superstore uses a pictogram to show the number of DVD players they sold over a 4-week period.

a) How many DVD players were sold in week 1?

b) In which week were the least number of DVD players sold?

c) How many DVD players were sold in week 3?

d) How many DVD players were sold in week 4?

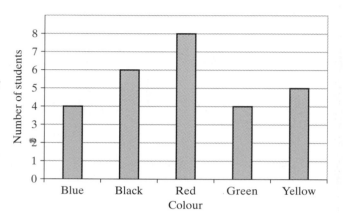

The superstore has data for two more weeks.

Week number	Number of DVD players sold
Week 5	16
Week 6	9

e) Add the data to a copy of the pictogram.

3 Fatima recorded the maximum temperatures in London and in Cape Town for the first six months of last year.
She produced a bar chart to compare the temperatures in the two cities.

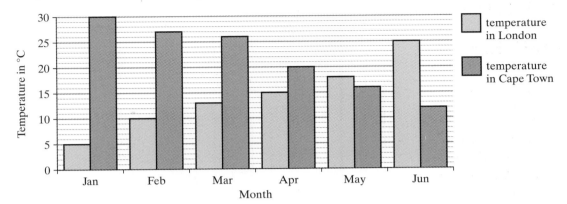

Use the dual bar chart to write down the following.

a) the maximum temperature in February in:
   (i) London   **(ii)** Cape Town

b) the month which had the highest maximum temperature in:
   (i) London   **(ii)** Cape Town

c) the month where the difference in maximum temperature between the two cities was:
   (i) the highest   **(ii)** the lowest
   and write down what this difference was.

d) the month where the highest maximum temperature in London became greater than the highest maximum temperature in Cape Town.

4 An art gallery had a sale of paintings.
The owner wrote down her total sales on each of the first five days of the sale.
The information is in the table below.

Day of the sale	Total sales
Monday	£4000
Tuesday	£3000
Wednesday	£1500
Thursday	£2250
Friday	£3750

Draw a pictogram to show this information.

Use ⊕ to represent £1000.

5 Six students, Ann, Ben, Con, Dani, Ed and Flo, each sat an examination in English, Mathematics and Science.
Each examination was marked out of 100.
Their teacher made a bar chart of their results.

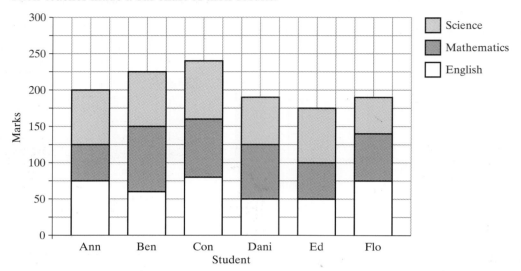

a) Which student got the highest total mark?
b) Which student got the highest Mathematics mark?
c) Two students got the same overall total.
   Write down the names of these two students.
d) One student got the same mark for all three subjects.
   Write down the name of this student.
e) What did Ann score for Science?
f) One student's best mark was for English.
   Write down the name of this student.

6 May counts the number of each of her favourite animals at the zoo.
Here are her results.

Type of animal	Number of animals
Giraffes	3
Lions	6
Monkeys	10
Polar Bears	3
Zebras	8

Draw a bar chart to show this information.

EXERCISE 3.2   H

1 Des asked 40 of his friends which was their favourite holiday destination in the UK. The table shows the results.

Draw a pie chart to illustrate this information.

City	Frequency
Blackpool	5
Bournemouth	7
Brighton	10
Falmouth	2
London	16

2 An optometrist wrote down what he sold to the 18 patients he saw on Saturday.

Draw a pie chart to illustrate this information.

Sales	Number
Spectacles	12
Contact lenses	4
Nothing	2

3 Patsy earns £30 a week doing various jobs. The table shows how she spent this money last week.

Draw a pie chart to illustrate this information.

Cinema	£7
Clothes	£12
Eating out	£8
Magazines	£3

4 Richard has 60 books on the bookshelves in his room.

Draw a pie chart to illustrate this data.

Type of book	Number of books
Science Fiction	17
Adventure	7
Reference	15
Novel	21

5 The table shows the spread of the ages of the members of a sports club.

Draw a pie chart to illustrate this data.

Age of members	Percentage
under 18	10
$18 \leqslant$ age < 25	18
$25 \leqslant$ age < 40	42
$40 \leqslant$ age < 60	22
60 or over	8

6 Craig draws a pie chart to show
how he uses his earnings in a typical month.

a) On what does he spend the most money?

Craig earns £720 per month after tax.

b) Work out how much Craig spends on:
(i) household bills
(ii) entertainment
(iii) rent
(iv) food

c) How much does Craig save each month?

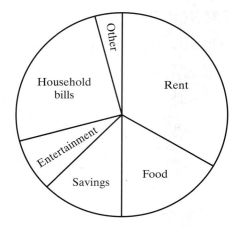

7 Janet and John each draw a pie chart to show how long they spent on their homework last weekend.

Janet spends 6 hours on her homework.
John spends 8 hours on his homework.

a) Write down the subject which is the mode for:
(i) Janet **(ii)** John

b) Work out how much time Janet spends on:
(i) Maths **(ii)** Art

c) Work out how much time John spends on Science.

d) Max says that Janet spends longer on her History homework than John because the angle for History on her pie chart is larger than the angle for History on John's pie chart.
Explain why Max is wrong.

EXERCISE 3.3 H

Do not use your calculator for Questions 1 and 2.

1 Here are the ages of the people staying in a hotel.
   a) Draw a frequency diagram to show this data.
   b) How many people were staying in the hotel?
   c) Write down the modal class interval.

Age	Frequency
$0 \leqslant \text{age} < 15$	15
$15 \leqslant \text{age} < 30$	11
$30 \leqslant \text{age} < 45$	47
$45 \leqslant \text{age} < 60$	32
$60 \leqslant \text{age} < 75$	10
$75 \leqslant \text{age} < 90$	4

2 Lara carries out a survey to find out the average amount of time students spend watching TV at the weekend.
   Here are her results.
   Draw a histogram of Lara's results.

Time in hours (h)	Frequency
$0 \leqslant h < 3$	5
$3 \leqslant h < 6$	14
$6 \leqslant h < 9$	22
$9 \leqslant h < 12$	8

You can use your calculator for Questions 3 and 4.

3 Maddy carried out a survey of the time, in minutes, it took students to get to school. The table shows the results of her survey.
   a) Draw a histogram to show this data.
   b) Write down the modal class interval.
   c) How many students were in Maddy's survey?
   d) How many students took less than half an hour to get to school?
   e) Find an estimate for the mean time, in minutes, it took students to get to school.

Time, t, in minutes	Frequency
$0 \leqslant t < 10$	11
$10 \leqslant t < 20$	34
$20 \leqslant t < 30$	26
$30 \leqslant t < 40$	15
$40 \leqslant t < 50$	4

4 A vet recorded the weight of 60 animals he saw over the weekend.
   a) Draw a histogram to show this data.
   b) Write down the modal class interval.
   c) Estimate the mean weight of the animals.
   d) Write down the class interval which contains the median.

Weight, w, in kg	Frequency
$0 \leqslant w < 3$	14
$3 \leqslant w < 6$	8
$6 \leqslant w < 9$	10
$9 \leqslant w < 12$	12
$12 \leqslant w < 15$	16

EXERCISE 3.4 H pt

1 Draw a frequency polygon for each of the sets of data given in Exercise 3.3.

You can use your calculator for Questions 2 and 3.

2 A football club carried out a survey of the ages of its 274 supporters at a football match. The results of the survey are shown in the table.

Age group, x years	Frequency
$0 \leqslant x < 10$	24
$10 \leqslant x < 20$	36
$20 \leqslant x < 30$	60
$30 \leqslant x < 40$	52
$40 \leqslant x < 50$	30
$50 \leqslant x < 60$	44
$60 \leqslant x < 70$	28

  a) Draw a frequency polygon to show this information.
  b) Which is the modal class?
  c) Find the class interval which contains the median.
  d) Find an estimate for the mean age.

3 Stand measured the heights of 60 boxes.
  Each height was recorded.
  The table shows information about these heights.

Height, (h cm)	Frequency
$0 \leqslant h < 20$	11
$20 \leqslant h < 40$	20
$40 \leqslant h < 60$	7
$60 \leqslant h < 80$	22

  a) Draw a frequency polygon to show this information.
  b) Work out an estimate for the mean height of these boxes.
  c) Write down the modal class interval.
  d) Find the class interval that contains the median.

EXERCISE 3.5

1 Lauren spent a year travelling.
She had a plane ticket to fly to
12 different countries in any order.
Each month she went to a different
country and recorded the
temperature there, in °C, on the
10th day of each month.
The graph shows this information.

a) What is the range of the
temperatures?

b) Write down the temperature in:
(i) July **(ii)** September.

c) Lauren takes two more readings:

Month	Nov	Dec
Temp	−5 °C	27 °C

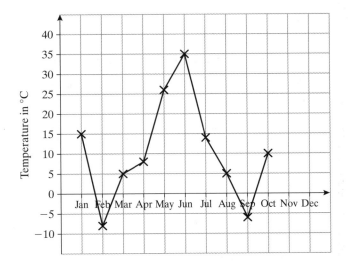

Add these measurements to a copy of Lauren's graph.

2 The time-series graph shows the
takings of a small company
one year.

a) What is the range of the
takings?

b) Which two months have the
same takings?

c) Here is the data for November
and December.

Month	Nov	Dec
Takings	£4500	£5700

Add the data to a copy of the time-series graph.

3 Mr Smith recorded the number of customers in his shop at particular times one Friday.
Here are his results.

Time	9 am	10 am	11 am	12 noon	1 pm	2 pm	3 pm	4 pm	5 pm
No. of customers	3	5	6	5	8	9	6	4	2

Draw a time-series graph for this data.

U1 CHAPTER 4

Probability

EXERCISE 4.1

1 The colours on a regular 5-sided spinner
are red, blue, yellow, green and purple.
Dean spins the spinner once.
Find the probability that it
  a) lands on red
  b) does **not** land on green
  c) lands on black.

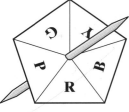

2 A football team is equally like to win, lose or draw a match.
On a copy of the probability line below mark with a letter **W** the probability that the football
team will win a match.

3 A fair dice has sides numbered 1, 2, 3, 4, 5 and 6.
The dice is thrown once.
On a copy of the probability line below:

  a) mark with a letter **A** the probability that the dice will land on an **even** number
  b) mark with a letter **B** the probability that the dice will land on a number **bigger** than 4
  c) mark with a letter **C** the probability that the dice will **not** land on a number bigger than 4
  d) mark with a letter **D** the probability that the dice will land on a number **bigger** than 0
  e) mark with a letter **E** the probability that the dice will land on a number **smaller** than 1

4 A regular eight-sided spinner has sides 1, 2, 3, 4, 5, 6, 7 and 8.
The spinner is spun once.
On a copy of the probability line below:

  a) mark with a letter **A** the probability that the spinner will
    land on an odd number
  b) mark with a letter **B** the probability that the spinner will land on a 5
  c) mark with a letter **C** the probability that the spinner will land on a number less than 10
  d) mark with a letter **D** the probability that the spinner will land on a factor of 15
  e) mark with a letter **E** the probability that the spinner will **not** land on a number less than 4
  f) mark with a letter **F** the probability that the spinner will land on a number bigger than 2

5 The probability that Deborah wins a competition is 0.27.
What is the probability that Deborah does not win the competition?

6 A bag contains 27 balls.
There are 10 blue balls and 13 red balls.
The rest of the balls are black.
A ball is chosen at random.
Find the probability that this ball is

    a) red   **b) not** blue   **c)** black.

7 The probability that I will be at school tomorrow is 0.93.
Work out the probability that I will **not** be at school tomorrow.

8 A drawer contains 40 socks.
10 of them are black, the rest are white or grey.
There are four times as many white socks as grey socks.
A sock is chosen at random.

    a) Work out the probability that it is black.
    b) Work out the probability that it is **not** black.
    c) Work out the probability that it is white.

EXERCISE 4.2 H

Do not use your calculator for Questions 1 and 2.

1 The diagram on the right shows some shapes.

    a) Copy and complete the table to show the
number of shapes in each category.

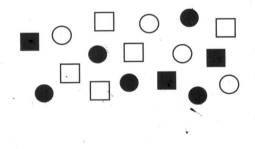

	Black	White	Total
Square			
Circle			
Total			

One of the shapes is chosen at random.
    b) Write down the probability that the shape is a circle.
    c) Write down the probability that the shape is **not** black.
    d) Write down the probability that the shape is a black square.

2 The two-way table shows some information about the numbers of people in a library.
    a) Copy and complete the two-way table.
A person in the library chooses a book.
    b) Work out the probability that the
person is a child.
One of the people in the library uses
the computer.
    c) Work out the probability that the
person is male.

	Adults	Children	Total
Male		7	18
Female	20		
Total			50

You can use your calculator for Questions 3 and 4.

3 A small play group has children aged 2 years, 3 years and 4 years. Darren wrote down the ages of the children that attended on Tuesday. The two-way table shows the results.

	2 years	3 years	4 years	Total
Boys	5	9	5	19
Girls	6	5	7	18
Total	11	14	12	37

   a) Find the probability that a child is a 2-year-old girl.
   b) Find the probability that a 4-year-old is a boy.
   c) Find the probability that a child is a 3-year-old.

4 A restaurant serves fruit salad, cheesecake or mousse for dessert.
Mr Chen keeps a record of what he serves on Sunday.
Every customer had one dessert.
The table shows some of this information.

	Fruit Salad	Cheesecake	Mousse	Total
Midday	10			
Evening		8		46
Total	28		25	70

   a) Copy and complete the two-way table.
   b) Find the probability that a customer had cheesecake for dessert.
   c) Find the probability that a customer had mousse for dessert in the evening.

EXERCISE 4.3 H pt

1 Two fair spinners are spun together. One spinner has five sides and the other has seven sides. The scores are **added** together.
   a) Copy and complete the table to show all the possible outcomes.
   b) What is the total number of possible outcomes?
   c) Write down the probability of getting a total of:
      (i)   9   (ii)   6
      (iii) 11   (iv) **not** 7
      (v)   an even number (vi) 10 or more

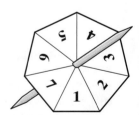

+	1	2	3	4	5	6	7
1	2						
2				6			
3		5					10
4							
5				9			12

2 A fair coin and a fair five-sided spinner
are thrown together.
   a) Write down all the possible outcomes of throwing
   the fair coin and the fair spinner.
   b) Write down the probability of getting:
   (i) a 'head' and a 'D'   **(ii)** a 'tail' and **not** a C.

3 Two fair spinners are spun together.
One spinner has five sides and the
other has eight sides.
The scores are **multiplied** together.
   a) Copy and complete the table to
   show all the possible outcomes.
   b) What is the total number of possible
   outcomes?
   c) Write down the probability of
   getting a total of:
   (i)   12
   (ii) 130
   (iii) 24
   (iv) **not** 18
   (v)   an odd number
   (vi) 25 or more.

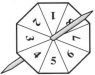

×	1	2	3	4	5	6	7	8
1	1							
2						12		
3		6					21	
4					20			
5								40

4 Gloria eats dinner in a restaurant.
She randomly selects a starter, a main
course and a dessert from this list.
   a) List all the possible outcomes of
   randomly selecting a starter, a
   main course and a dessert.
   b) Write down the probability that Gloria will eat:
   (i) pâté   **(ii)** soup and chicken   **(iii)** pâté, lamb and cherry pie.

Starter	Main course	Dessert
Soup	Chicken	Cherry pie
Pâté	Lamb	Fruit salad

5 Two fair spinners are spun together.
One spinner has four sides and the other has
six sides.
The **difference** between the two scores is found.
   a) Complete the table to show all the
   possible outcomes.
   b) What is the total number of
   possible outcomes?
   c) Write down the probability of
   getting a total of:
   (i)   1
   (ii) 5
   (iii) 2
   (iv) **not** 0
   (v)   an even number
   (vi) 4 or less

Difference	1	2	3	4	5	6
1	0					
2			1			
3					2	
4	3					

6 Liz picks one shape from Box P.
She then picks one shape from Box Q.

One pair she could pick is (white rectangle, white circle).

a) List all the pairs Liz could pick.
b) What is the probability that Liz picks (white rectangle, black circle)?
c) What is the probability that Liz picks a white circle?
d) What is the probability that Liz picks two circles?

7 Geoff picks one number from each of Boxes A, B and C.
One trio he could pick is (2, 4, 1).

  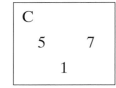

a) List all the trios Geoff could pick.
b) Write down the probability that:
   (i) Geoff picks (2, 4, 1)   (ii) Geoff picks a '7'   (iii) Geoff picks an '8'
   (iv) Geoff picks a '9' and a '5'   (v) Geoff picks three numbers that total 24

EXERCISE 4.4   H

Do not use your calculator for Questions 1–4.

1 The probability that Jean is late for work is 0.1.
How many times would you expect Jean to be late for work in 30 working days?

2 A fair coin is thrown 300 times.
How many times would you expect it to show 'heads'?

3 Simon has a biased dice.
Simon tosses the dice 100 times.
Here are his results.

Result	1	2	3	4	5	6
Frequency	42	27	2	3	21	5

Write down the experimental probability of the dice landing on:
a) 5   b) 1   c) an odd number

4 The probability of a biased coin showing 'heads' is 0.25.
a) What is the probability of the coin showing 'tails'?

The coin is thrown 40 times.
b) Work out an estimate for the number of times it will show 'tails'.

You can use your calculator for Questions 5–8.

5 The probability that Colin will put up his hand in a lesson is $\frac{4}{5}$.

   a) What is the probability that Colin will not put up his hand in a lesson?

   Colin goes to 40 lessons each week.

   b) Work out an estimate for the number of times Colin will put up his hand in a week.

6 There are 500 sweets in a jar. 100 of the sweets are red.

   The rest are orange, yellow or green.

   Ted takes a sweet at random from the jar and puts it back.

   a) Calculate the probability that Ted takes a red sweet.

   Tessa takes 50 sweets at random from the jar.

   20 of these sweets are orange.

   b) Estimate how many orange sweets are in the jar.

7 A box contains just 1p coins, 2p coins and 5p coins.

   There are 200 coins in the box and 50 of these are 2p coins.

   Miriam randomly takes a coin from the box and then puts it back.

   a) Work out the probability that the coin Miriam takes is a 2p coin.

   Miriam then randomly takes 40 coins from the box. 10 of these were 5p coins.

   b) Estimate the total number of 5p coins in the box.

8 In the sixth form at Gravitas School there are 63 boys and 78 girls.

   a) A student is chosen at random from the sixth form.
      Work out the probability that the student is a girl.

   b) There are 1200 students altogether at Gravitas School.
      Estimate the total number of girls at the school.

   c) Explain why your estimate might not be very reliable.

EXERCISE 4.5   H

1 When Lara returns from school she either does her homework or watches TV or tidies her room
or has a snack.

   The probability that Lara does her homework is 0.2.

   The probability that Lara watches TV is 0.4.

   The probability that Lara has a snack is 0.3.

   What is the probability that Lara tidies her room?

2 Joan either has coffee or tea or hot chocolate in the morning.

   The probability that Joan has coffee is 0.4.

   The probability that Joan has tea is 0.25.

   What is the probability that Joan has hot chocolate in the morning?

3 Traffic lights show either red or amber or green.

   The probability that the traffic lights show red is 0.43.

   The probability that the traffic lights show green is 0.46.

   a) What is the probability that the traffic lights show amber?

   There are 20 traffic lights on Janet's way to work.

   b) Work out an estimate for the number of times the traffic lights will show green.

4 A bag contains black, white, pink and orange counters.
A counter is drawn at random.
The table shows the probabilities of the counter being each of the four colours.

Colour	Black	White	Pink	Orange
Probability	$\frac{8}{23}$		$\frac{3}{23}$	$\frac{2}{23}$

a) What is the probability of the counter being white?
b) What is the probability of the counter being black or pink?
c) What is the probability of the counter **not** being orange?

5 A biased dice shows scores of 1, 2, 3, 4, 5, 6 with these probabilities.

Score	1	2	3	4	5	6
Probability	0.23		0.3	0.18	0.1	0.05

The dice is rolled once. Find the probability that the score obtained is:
a) 2   b) not 4   c) 5 or 6   d) an odd number.

6 When Andrew goes to work he is either early, on time or late.
The incomplete table shows some probabilities.

	Early	On time	Late
Probability	$\frac{27}{100}$		$\frac{6}{100}$

a) What is the probability that Andrew arrives on time?
b) Which of the three outcomes is most likely?
c) Find the probability that Andrew is **not** late for work.

7 There are four types of animals I might see in my garden.
The table shows the probability that a fox or a hedgehog or a squirrel or a
cat will be seen in my garden. No two animals are ever in the garden at the same time.

Type of creature	Fox	Hedgehog	Squirrel	Cat
Probability	0.15		0.4	0.28

a) Copy and complete the probability table.
b) Which type of animal do I see most often in my garden?

An animal is observed at random.
Find the probability that:
c) it is **not** a cat,
d) it is a fox or a squirrel.

8 Bertha has three children, Robert, Johnny and Stephen.
Every Friday night Bertha has dinner with one of her children.
The probability that she has dinner with Robert is 0.28 and the probability
that she has dinner with Johnny is 0.3.
a) Work out the probability that she has dinner with Stephen.
b) Work out the probability that she does **not** have dinner with Stephen.

9 A biased spinner gives scores of 1, 2, 3 or 4.
The probability of getting 1 is 0.37.
The probability of getting 2 is 0.18.
The probability of getting 4 is 0.2.
  a) Calculate the probability of getting an even score.
  b) Work out the probability of getting a score of 3.

10 Sue often partners Janet or Don at tennis.
The probability that she will partner Janet is 0.38.
The probability that she will partner Don is 0.17.
  a) Work out the probability that she will partner Janet or Don at tennis.
  b) Work out the probability that she will **not** partner either of these two at tennis.

11 Alex goes to the cinema.
He can choose from a comedy, a drama, a science fiction movie or a horror movie.
The table shows the probability that Alex will choose a particular type of movie.

Type of movie	Comedy	Drama	Science fiction	Horror
Probability	0.17	0.23	x	x

  a) Find the probability that he chooses a comedy or a drama.
  b) Find the probability that he chooses a science fiction movie or a horror movie.

The probability he will choose to see a science fiction movie is the same as the probability he will choose to see a horror movie.
  c) Find the probability he will choose to see a horror movie.

12 The junior football team at Roddington School is picked from students in Years 7 or 8 or 9.
Mr Right selects the junior football teams. The probability that he might select a student from Years 7 or 8 is shown in the table below.

Year group	Year 7	Year 8	Year 9
Probability	24%	32%	

  a) Copy and complete the probability table.
Mr Right needs to pick 50 students for some junior football teams.
  b) Estimate the number of Year 8 students he is likely to pick.

13 A drawer contains black, white, blue and brown socks.
In a probability experiment, one sock is chosen at random, and removed from the drawer.
Its colour is noted, and it is returned to the drawer.
The table shows some probabilities for this experiment.

Colour	Black	White	Blue	Brown
Probability	0.36	0.31	0.1	

  a) Find the probability of choosing a brown sock.
The experiment is carried out 300 times.
  b) Estimate the number of times a white sock is chosen.

U1 CHAPTER 5

Further statistics (Higher Tier only)

EXERCISE 5.1

1 The table shows the number of children in each of 4 groups at a club.

A stratified sample of size 40 is to be taken from the club.

Alix says that this means you take 10 from each group.

(i) Explain why Alix is wrong.

(ii) Work out how many students from each group should be in the sample.

Group	Number of children
A	27
B	38
C	13
D	25

2 A newspaper editor wants to find out people's opinions about a law that has just been passed in Parliament.

I'm going to write an article about the law and invite readers of the paper to write in and express their views about the new law.

Reporter A

Im going to stand in the street and ask every tenth person what they think of the new law.

Reporter B

Explain which of these methods is the better one.

3 Davin is studying the number of matches in boxes of Rover matches.
He wants to see if the number of matches in each box is the same.
He goes to his local newsagent and buys 50 boxes of Rover matches.
He then takes them home and counts the numbers in each box.
Explain briefly whether you think this is a good sampling method.

4 The table shows the number of students in each year group at Wendower School.
There are 800 students at the school altogether.

Age group	Year 7	Year 8	Year 9	Year 10	Year 11
Number of students	185	199	226	82	108

Mavis wants to take a stratified sample of 60 students from the school.
Draw up a table to show how many students she should select from each year group.

5 David and Graham are planning a coursework exercise.
They want to find out about the student absences at different schools in London.

> I'm going to sample four schools in each borough.

David

> I'm going to sample 30% of the schools in London.

Graham

Explain why one of these methods is much better than the other.

 EXERCISE 5.2

1 320 students took a test.
The cumulative frequency graph gives information about their marks.

Work out an estimate for the interquartile range of their marks.

[Edexcel]

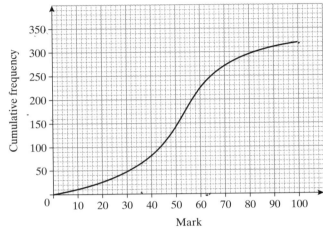

2 Bill asked 80 students how many hours each of them spent doing homework last week.
He used the information to draw this cumulative frequency graph.

Use the cumulative frequency graph to find an estimate for:
a) the median number of hours
b) the number of students who spent more than 7 hours on their homework. [Edexcel]

3 The cumulative frequency diagram below gives information about the prices of 120 houses.
  a) Find an estimate for the number of houses with prices less than £130 000.
  b) Work out an estimate for the interquartile range of the prices of the 120 houses.

Prices of houses (£)

[Edexcel]

4 Rob recorded the times, in minutes, it took some students to walk to school.

He used his results to work out this information.

Shortest time = 4 minutes
Lower quartile = 12 minutes
Median time = 19 minutes
Interquartile range = 20 minutes
Range of time = 53 minutes

On a copy of the grid draw a box plot to show this information.

Minutes

5 The table shows information about the number of hours that 120 children used a computer last week.

Number of hours (h)	Frequency
$0 < h \leqslant 2$	10
$2 < h \leqslant 4$	15
$4 < h \leqslant 6$	30
$6 < h \leqslant 8$	35
$8 < h \leqslant 10$	25
$10 < h \leqslant 12$	5

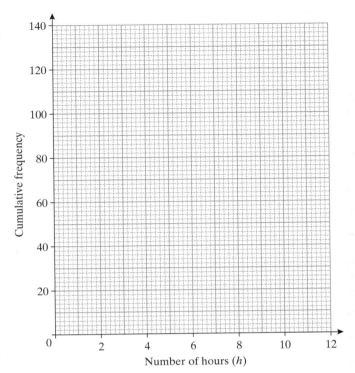

a) Complete a copy of the cumulative frequency table.

Number of hours (h)	Cumulative frequency
$0 < h \leqslant 2$	10
$2 < h \leqslant 4$	
$4 < h \leqslant 6$	
$6 < h \leqslant 8$	
$8 < h \leqslant 10$	
$10 < h \leqslant 12$	

b) On a copy of the grid above, draw a cumulative frequency graph for your table.

c) Use your graph to find an estimate for the number of children who used a computer for **less** than 7 hours last week.

[Edexcel]

6 The box plot gives information about the number of hours some students watched TV last weekend.

Use the box plot to work out, in hours:

a) the median time

b) the range of the times

c) the interquartile range of the times.

7 Here are four cumulative frequency diagrams.

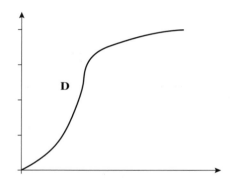

Here are four box plots.

P

Q

R

S

For each box plot, write down the letter of the appropriate cumulative frequency diagram.

P and ....

Q and ....

R and ....

S and ....

EXERCISE 5.3

1 7 cats have a mean weight of 3.4 kg. Another cat weighs 4.2 kg.
Work out the mean weight of all 8 cats.

2 10 pieces of cheese have a mean weight of 320 g.
Another 8 pieces of cheese have a mean weight of 545 g.
Work out the mean weight of all 18 pieces of cheese.

3 There are 15 players in a football team.
6 of the players have a mean height of 1.7 m.
The other 9 players have a mean height of 1.62 m.
Find the mean height for all 15 players.

4 There are 400 students at a school. The students take a Mathematics exam.
The table below shows the results.

	Number of students	Mean mark
Girls	230	63%
Boys	170	67%

Calculate the mean mark for all 400 students.

5 The mean number of children in 7 families in a street is 2.8 children.
The mean number of children in the 7 families in the next street is 1.75 children.

Leo says, 'The mean number of children in all 14 families is $\dfrac{2.8 + 1.75}{2} = 2.275$ children.'

Explain carefully whether Leo is right or wrong.

6 The mean weight loss of the 25 adults at a slimming class on Monday was 1.72 kg.
Another adult arrived late and after he was weighed the mean increased to 1.74 kg.
Work out the weight loss of the adult who arrived late.

7 To get a distinction, Katrina has to get an average of 80 marks over 10 examinations.
In the first 9 examinations Katrina obtained a mean score of 81 marks.
Work out the least number of marks she needs to score in the tenth examination in order to
obtain a distinction.

8 One year the mean monthly rainfall in a city in India was 10 cm.
The mean monthly rainfall for the first 7 months was only 5 cm.
Work out the mean monthly rainfall for the next 5 months.

EXERCISE 5.4

1 The table shows the number of umbrellas sold each quarter by a small shop.
The data was collected from January 1997 to December 1999.

1997				1998				1999			
Jan to Mar	Apr to Jun	Jul to Sep	Oct to Dec	Jan to Mar	Apr to Jun	Jul to Sep	Oct to Dec	Jan to Mar	Apr to Jun	Jul to Sep	Oct to Dec
27	15	10	20	28	14	11	21	30	16	13	22
	18	18.25	18								

a) Work out the four-quarter moving averages for the data.
The first three have been done for you.
b) Plot a time series graph of the original data.
c) On the same axes, plot a time series graph of the moving averages.
What do the graphs show you about the seasonal variation in the number of umbrellas sold?

2 The table shows the number of absences at a school over a period of three weeks.

Week 1					Week 2					Week 3				
Mon	Tue	Wed	Thu	Fri	Mon	Tue	Wed	Thu	Fri	Mon	Tue	Wed	Thu	Fri
18	10	7	6	16	20	13	8	8	18	21	14	8	10	20
		11.4	11.8	12.4										

a) Work out the five-day moving averages for the data.
Explain why there are only 11 of these values, not 15.
The first three have been done for you.
b) Plot a time series graph of the original data.
What can you say about the absences on different days of the week?
c) Plot a time series graph of the moving averages.
What can you say about the weekly average absences?

3 The table shows the average number of school dinners sold each day by the school canteen over a period of four years.

Year	2001			2002			2003			2004		
Term	1st	2nd	3rd	1st	2nd	3rd	1st	2nd	3rd	1st	2nd	3rd
	150	127	101	138	121	89	135	118	86	132	109	77
	126	122	120									

a) Plot a time series graph of the data.
Describe whether you can see any seasonal variation in the number of school dinners sold.
b) Calculate a set of three-value moving averages from the data.
Three of the ten values have been done for you.
c) Plot a time series graph of the moving averages.
d) Add a straight line to your graph to indicate the underlying trend.

EXERCISE 5.5

1   Justin is a florist.
    He measured 100 flowers and recorded the heights to the nearest centimetre.
    The table shows information about the heights, h, of the 100 flowers.

Height, h	Frequency, f
$0 \leqslant h < 20$	24
$20 \leqslant h < 40$	38
$40 \leqslant h < 60$	16
$60 \leqslant h < 80$	12
$80 \leqslant h < 100$	10

   a)   Draw a frequency polygon to show this information.
        Use graph paper with the *frequency* axis 8 cm high, numbered from 0 to 40, and the *height*
        axis 10 cm wide, numbered from 0 to 100.

   b)   Work out an estimate for the mean height of these flowers.

   c)   Find the class interval that contains the median.

2   The table gives information about how long, in minutes, some people took to read a magazine.

Time (t) in minutes	Frequency
$0 < t \leqslant 10$	20
$10 < t \leqslant 15$	30
$15 < t \leqslant 30$	60
$30 < t \leqslant 60$	90

   Use the table to draw a histogram that shows this information.

3 A teacher asked some Year 10 students how long they spent doing homework each night. The histogram was drawn from this information.

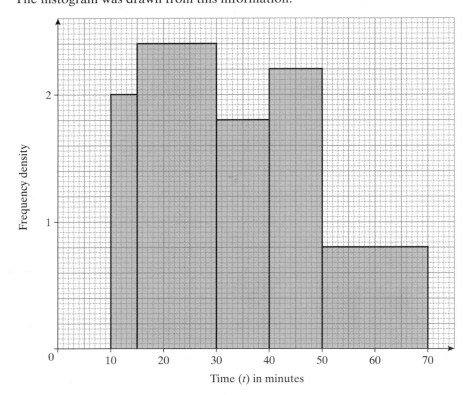

Use the histogram to complete the table.

Time (t) in minutes	Frequency
$10 \leqslant t < 15$	10
$15 \leqslant t < 30$	
$30 \leqslant t < 40$	
$40 \leqslant t < 50$	
$50 \leqslant t < 70$	

4 A teacher asked some students how much time they spent using a mobile phone one week. The histogram was drawn from this information.

Use the histogram to complete a copy of the table.

Time (t) in hours	Frequency
$0 \leqslant t < \frac{1}{2}$	
$\frac{1}{2} \leqslant t < 1$	
$1 \leqslant t < 2$	30
$2 \leqslant t < 3$	
$3 \leqslant t < 5$	

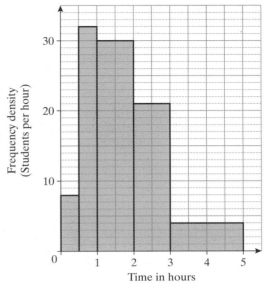

[Edexcel]

5 Some students at Highfliers School took a Mathematics examination.
The unfinished table and histogram show some information about their marks.

Mark ($x\%$)	Frequency
$0 < x \leqslant 40$	10
$40 < x \leqslant 60$	40
$60 < x \leqslant 75$	45
$75 < x \leqslant 85$	60
$85 < x \leqslant 95$	
$95 < x \leqslant 100$	25

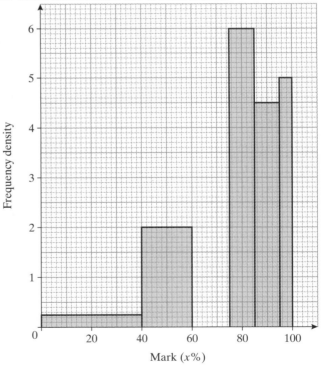

a) Use the information in the table to complete a copy of the histogram.
b) Use the information in the histogram to complete the table.

[Edexcel]

U1 CHAPTER 6

Further probability (Higher Tier only)

EXERCISE 6.1

1 A box contains coins. A coin is chosen at random.
The table shows the probabilities of the coin being of a certain value.

Value	1p	5p	10p	20p	50p
Probability	0.1	0.35	0.2	0.05	0.3

Find the probability that the chosen coin is:
a) a 10p coin
b) a 20p or 50p coin
c) not a 5p coin.

2 A spinner can land on Red, Blue, Pink, Green or Black.
The table shows the probabilities that the spinner will land on Red, Blue, Pink or Green.

Colour	Red	Blue	Pink	Green	Black
Probability	0.25	0.1	0.3	0.14	

Find the probability that the spinner lands on:
a) Pink
b) Blue or Green
c) Black

3 Debbie partners either Ivan, Joshua or Leo in a game.
The probability that she will partner Ivan is 0.4. The probability that she will partner Leo is 0.5.
Work out the probability that in a game Debbie will partner:
a) Ivan or Leo
b) Joshua or Leo.

4 When Gary goes to work he is either early, on time or late.
The probability that he will be on time is 0.16 and the probability that he is early is equal to the probability that he will be late.
Work out the probability that:
a) Gary will be late
b) Gary will be early or on time.

5 There are six pieces of paper in a hat. Each piece of paper has a letter written on it.
The letter is either A or B or C or D or E or F.
A piece of paper is picked at random from the hat.
The table shows the probability that a particular letter will be chosen.

Letter	A	B	C	D	E	F
Probability	0.13	0.02	0.15	0.3	0.24	0.16

Work out the probability that the letter:
a) will not be B
b) will be a vowel.

EXERCISE 6.2

1 The probability that Brad will be injured in a football match is 0.13.
The probability that Marc will be injured in a football match is 0.4.
Calculate the probability that:
a) Brad and Marc will both be injured in a football match
b) Brad will be injured and Marc will not be injured in a football match.

2 A fair spinner has four sides numbered 2, 3, 4 and 5.
It is spun twice and the numbers are added together.
a) Draw up a two-way table to show the possible combinations of scores.
b) Find the probability that the total score is 8.
c) What is the most likely total score?

3 A bag contains 5 blue marbles, 2 red marbles and 6 green marbles.
A marble is chosen at random. It is then replaced, and a second marble is chosen.
a) Work out the probability that the first marble is **not** red.
b) Work out the probability that both marbles are blue.

4 Terri has a fair three-sided spinner, with the numbers 3, 4 and 5 written on it.
She also has a fair four-sided spinner, with the numbers 2, 3, 5 and 6 written on it.
Terri spins both spinners and multiplies the two numbers together.
a) Draw up a two-way table to show the possible results.
b) Work out the probability that the product of the two numbers is 15.
c) Work out the probability that the product of the two numbers is even.

5 Garth throws a big dice and a small dice.
Both dice are normal six-sided fair dice, labelled with the numbers 1, 2, 3, 4, 5, 6.
a) Write down the probability that the small dice shows a number bigger than 6.
b) Work out the probability that the big dice shows a larger number than the small dice.
c) Work out the probability that Garth throws two even numbers.

6 A box contains coloured pencils which are red or blue or pink.
Jilly takes a pencil from the box at random and puts it back.
The probability that the pencil is red is 0.6.
The probability that it is pink is 0.1.
a) Write down the probability that Jilly takes a blue pencil.

Ian takes two pencils from the box and puts them back.
b) Work out the probability that Ian takes two red pencils.

Benji takes three pencils from the box.
c) Work out the probability that the first two pencils are the same colour but the third one is not.

7 In a large box of light bulbs, $\frac{1}{20}$ are defective.
The manager of the store takes two light bulbs from the box.
a) Calculate the probability that the first light bulb is defective and the second one is not.
b) Calculate the probability that they are both defective.
Give your answers as exact fractions.

8 Each school day Mrs Kothare selects one girl and one boy at random, from some classes, to show her their homework diaries.
The table shows the probabilities of each student being chosen.

Girls	Year 7	Year 8	Year 9	Year 10
Probability	0.3	0.16	0.42	0.12

Boys	Year 7	Year 8	Year 9	Year 10
Probability	0.2	0.29	0.21	0.3

a) Calculate the probability that Mrs Kothare chooses a girl from Year 9 and a boy from Year 10.
b) Calculate the probability that she chooses a girl and boy from Year 10.
There are 200 school days one year.
c) Estimate the number of days Mrs Kothare chooses two Year 7 students.

EXERCISE 6.3

1 Patrick goes for two job interviews. The probability he will be offered the first job is 0.3 and the probability he will be offered the second job is 0.12.

a) Copy and complete the tree diagram to show the possible outcomes of Patrick's job interviews.

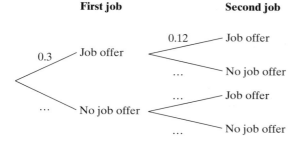

b) Work out the probability that Patrick is offered both jobs.
c) Work out the probability that Patrick is offered only one job.

2 Sabia drives to work each morning.
She passes two sets of traffic lights on the way to work.
The probability that a set of traffic lights is green is $\frac{3}{5}$.
a) Draw a tree diagram to represent the possible outcomes of the two traffic lights.
b) Work out the probability that both sets of traffic lights are green.
c) Work out the probability that the first set of traffic lights is **not** green and the second set of traffic lights is green.
d) Work out the probability that just one of the two sets of traffic lights is green.

3 Jean sells two pairs of glasses.
The glasses have either single vision lenses, bifocal lenses or varifocal lenses.
The probability that Jean will sell glasses with single vision lenses is 0.4.
The probability that Jean will sell glasses with bifocal lenses is 0.35.

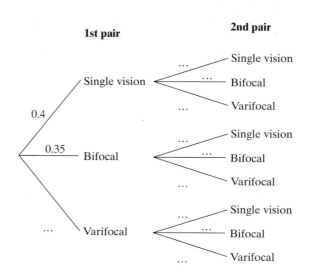

a) Copy and complete the tree diagram.
b) Find the probability that Jean sells one pair of glasses with bifocal lenses and one pair with varifocal lenses.
c) Find the probability that Jean does **not** sell two pairs of single vision lenses.

4 Jodi has 30 DVDs, 6 of which are musicals.
Wayne has 40 DVDs, 5 of which are musicals.
Jodi and Wayne choose one DVD each at random from their own collections.
  a) Write down the probability that Jodi chooses a musical.
  b) Write down the probability that Wayne chooses a musical.
  c) Draw a tree diagram to illustrate their choices.
  d) Hence find the probability that at least one of them does **not** choose a musical.

5 Louis is a fantastic golfer.
The probability that he gets a hole-in-one (the ball in the hole with one hit) is 0.2.
Louis plays three holes at golf.
  a) Illustrate the possible results of getting a hole-in-one, or not, on a tree diagram.
  b) Work out the probability that he gets three holes-in-one.
  c) Work out the probability that he gets exactly one hole-in-one.

6 Deborah (D) and Toby (T) play two games of Snakes and Ladders.
The probability that Deborah will win the first game is 0.1 and the probability that she will win the second game is 0.4.
  a) Copy and complete the tree diagram.

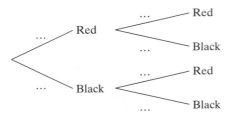

  b) Calculate the probability that:
    (i) Deborah will win both games
    (ii) they will each win one game.

EXERCISE 6.4

1 A drawer contains 12 socks. 3 of the socks are red and the rest are black.
Ali is going to take two socks at random from the drawer, **without** replacement.

  a) Copy and complete the tree diagram.
  b) Work out the probability that Ali will take two red socks.
  c) Work out the probability that Ali will take two socks of the same colour.

2   In a class of 30 students, 9 wear glasses and 21 do not wear glasses.
    Two students are chosen at random.
    a) Illustrate the situation with a tree diagram.
    b) Calculate the probability that both students wear glasses.
    c) Calculate the probability that at least one student wears glasses.

3   A small box contains 21 chocolates.
    15 are milk chocolates and the rest are plain chocolates.
    Two chocolates are picked at random, without replacement.
    a) Draw a tree diagram to show this information.
    b) Calculate the probability that one milk chocolate and one plain chocolate are picked.

4   Tanya forecasts the results of 3 tennis matches.
    Work out the probability that she forecasts the correct result in all 3 matches.

5   A box contains 25 smarties. 8 are red, 6 are yellow and the rest are green.
    Two smarties are chosen at random, without replacement.
    a) Draw a tree diagram to show this information.
    b) Calculate the probability that the two smarties are **not** the same colour.

6   In a bowl of fruit there are 3 bananas, 4 oranges and 5 apples.
    Two pieces of fruit are picked at random from the bowl.
    a) Draw a tree diagram to show this information.
    b) Find the probability that 2 oranges are picked.
    c) Work out the probability that two **different** pieces of fruit are picked.

7   There are 15 students in a class.
    9 of the students are right-handed, and the other 6 are left-handed.
    a) Two of the 15 students are chosen at random.
            Find the probability that they are both right-handed.
    b) Three of the 15 students are chosen at random.
            Find the probability that they are all left-handed.

UNIT 2

U2 CHAPTER 1

Working with whole numbers

All Exercises in this Chapter are Stage 1. Exercises 1.1, 1.2, 1.3 and 1.4 are also Stage 2.

 EXERCISE 1.1

Work out the answers to these problems in your head.

1 38 + 27 + 594 + 12   **2** 234 + 356 + 41   **3** 55 + 739 + 184

4 743 + 136 + 87   **5** 32 + 33 + 34 + 35 + 36   **6** 26 + 53 + 17 + 49

7 38 + 49 + 795   **8** 437 − 99   **9** 138 + 381

10 573 − 399

Use any written method to work out the answers to these problems. Show your working clearly.

11 825 + 67   **12** 170 + 376   **13** 826 − 394

14 890 − 368   **15** 2647 + 3691   **16** 509 + 417 + 32

17 7302 − 4798   **18** 7007 − 3678

19 An aircraft can carry 326 passengers when all the seats are full, but today 78 of the seats are empty. How many passengers are on the aircraft today?

20 The attendances at a cinema complex were 379 (Monday), 526 (Tuesday) and 804 (Wednesday). How many people attended in total?

 EXERCISE 1.2

Use short multiplication to work out the answers to these calculations.

1 235 × 5   **2** 482 × 7   **3** 384 × 3   **4** 168 × 9

5 514 × 6   **6** 690 × 7   **7** 723 × 8   **8** 888 × 4

Use any written method to work out the answers to these problems. Show your working clearly.

9 573 × 21   **10** 389 × 32   **11** 704 × 45   **12** 616 × 82

13 461 × 63   **14** 902 × 56   **15** 157 × 97   **16** 833 × 74

17 A company has 36 coaches and each coach can carry 43 passengers. How many passengers in total can all the coaches carry?

18 I have a set of 24 encyclopaedias. Each one has 288 pages.
How many pages are there in the whole set?

19 Jon buys 18 stamps at 26 pence each and 14 stamps at 47 pence each.
How much does he spend in total?

20 A cinema has 43 rows with 26 seats in each row.
Calculate the total number of seats in the cinema.

 EXERCISE 1.3

Use short division to work out the answers to these calculations.
(Three of them should leave remainders.)

1 $812 \div 6$	**2** $1364 \div 4$	**3** $9279 \div 9$	**4** $6832 \div 7$
5 $6895 \div 5$	**6** $3456 \div 3$	**7** $2394 \div 8$	**8** $500 \div 6$

Use long division to work out the answers to these problems. Show your working clearly.
(Only the last two should leave remainders.)

9 $1323 \div 21$	**10** $1984 \div 16$	**11** $9750 \div 25$	**12** $7776 \div 32$
13 $6372 \div 18$	**14** $9196 \div 22$	**15** $5367 \div 31$	**16** $4055 \div 27$

17 £1164 is shared out equally between 6 people. How much does each one receive?

18 May makes 17 necklaces out of 2159 beads. Each necklace has the same number of beads.
How many beads are there on each necklace?

19 A teacher shares out 868 sheets of paper equally amongst her class of 28 students.
How many sheets of paper does each student receive?

20 Havering School has 434 students divided equally into 14 classes.
How many students are in each class?

 EXERCISE 1.4

Without using a calculator, work out the answers to the following.

1 $-3 + (-4)$	**2** $9 + (-5)$	**3** $7 - (-1)$	**4** $-6 - (-2)$
5 $-7 + 3$	**6** $-9 - (6)$	**7** $-1 - -3$	**8** $-8 + -5$
9 $(2) - +3$	**10** $-5 + -5$	**11** $3 - -4$	**12** $-4 - +5$
13 $1 + -6$	**14** $-6 - -1$	**15** -2×-8	**16** $-7 \times +9$
17 5×-6	**18** $-16 \div -4$	**19** $-7 \div 7$	**20** $24 \div -8$

21 Arrange these in order of size, smallest first: 0, −9, 2, 7, −4.

22 Arrange these in order of size, smallest first: −24, −28, 15, 25, −10.

23 What number lies midway between −18 and −32?

24 What number lies one-third of the way from −5 to 25?

EXERCISE 1.5 **1**

1 List all the prime numbers from 22 to 65 inclusive.
You should find there are ten such prime numbers altogether.

2 Use your result from question **1** to help answer these questions:
  a) How many primes are there between 40 and 60 inclusive?
  b) What is the next prime number above 55?
  c) Find two prime numbers that add together to make 120.
  d) Write 123 as a product of two prime factors.

3 Use the factor tree method to obtain the prime factorisation of:
  a) 75   **b)** 84   **c)** 420

4 Use the factor tree method to obtain the prime factorisation of:
  a) 24   **b)** 81   **c)** 192
What do you notice about all three of your answers?

5 When 250 is written as a product of primes, the result is $5^x \times y$ where x and y are positive integers. Find the values of x and y.

EXERCISE 1.6 **1**

1 Use the method of inspection to write down the highest common factor (HCF) of each pair of numbers. Check your result in each case.
  a) 15 and 18   **b)** 48 and 60   **c)** 30 and 75
  d) 16 and 24   **e)** 44 and 66   **f)** 34 and 170

2 Write each of the following numbers as a product of prime factors.
Hence find the highest common factor of each pair of numbers.
  a) 35 and 28   **b)** 42 and 105   **c)** 24 and 90
  d) 66 and 220   **e)** 90 and 105   **f)** 140 and 175

3 Use Euclid's method to find the highest common factor of each pair of numbers.
  a) 10 and 15   **b)** 40 and 48   **c)** 45 and 60
  d) 28 and 42   **e)** 33 and 55   **f)** 38 and 190

EXERCISE 1.7   1

Find the lowest common multiple (LCM) of each of these pairs of numbers.
You may use whichever method you prefer.

1 15 and 25	**2** 18 and 27	**3** 10 and 35	**4** 14 and 26
5 4 and 34	**6** 21 and 28	**7** 22 and 33	**8** 18 and 24
9 30 and 45	**10** 36 and 45	**11** 42 and 63	**12** 20 and 50
13 75 and 175	**14** 69 and 92	**15** 39 and 65	**16** 8 and 32

17 a) Write 90 and 210 as products of their prime factors.
 b) Hence find the LCM of 90 and 210.

18 a) Write 93 and 124 as products of their prime factors.
 b) Hence find the LCM of 93 and 124.
 c) Find also the HCF of 93 and 124.

19 a) Write 6, 9 and 15 as products of their prime factors.
 b) Work out the HCF of 6, 9 and 15.
 c) Work out the LCM of 6, 9 and 15.

20 a) Write 25, 30 and 80 as products of their prime factors.
 b) Work out the HCF of 25, 30 and 80.
 c) Work out the LCM of 25, 30 and 80.

21 Michael has two friends who sometimes come round to his house.
 Keith comes round once every 3 days and Peter comes round once every 7 days.
 How often are both friends at Michael's house together?

22 Christine owns three sports cars.
 She cleans the Ferrari once every 6 days, the Lotus once every 14 days and the Porsche once every 21 days.
 Today she cleaned all three cars.
 When will she next clean all three cars on the same day?

U2 CHAPTER 2

Fractions and decimals

The Exercises in this Chapter are all Stage 1 and Stage 2.

 EXERCISE 2.1

Write these fractions in their simplest form.

1 $\frac{12}{48}$ **2** $\frac{24}{72}$ **3** $\frac{8}{20}$ **4** $\frac{22}{77}$ **5** $\frac{5}{35}$ **6** $\frac{42}{84}$

7 $\frac{50}{175}$ **8** $\frac{39}{45}$ **9** $\frac{72}{96}$ **10** $\frac{18}{27}$ **11** $\frac{10}{35}$ **12** $\frac{42}{70}$

Arrange these fractions in order of size, smallest first.

13 $\frac{3}{4}, \frac{5}{6}, \frac{7}{10}, \frac{11}{15}$ **14** $\frac{4}{9}, \frac{1}{3}, \frac{1}{4}, \frac{5}{12}$ **15** $\frac{2}{5}, \frac{1}{6}, \frac{3}{10}, \frac{4}{15}$

 EXERCISE 2.2

Work out the answers to these calculations without a calculator.

1 6.27×0.3 **2** 5.09×0.2 **3** 2.8×3.6 **4** 5.7×1.4

5 7.14×3.8 **6** 6.71×9.2 **7** 0.04×0.1 **8** 0.7×0.02

9 $44.45 \div 7$ **10** $2.675 \div 0.5$ **11** $30.66 \div 2.1$ **12** $0.36 \div 0.9$

13 $29.12 \div 1.3$ **14** $0.6413 \div 0.01$ **15** $30.566 \div 3.1$ **16** $20.91 \div 0.17$

17 Given that $28 \times 64 = 1792$, work out the values of
 a) 6.4×2.8 **b)** 0.64×28 **c)** 640×280

18 Given that $215 \times 38 = 8170$, work out the values of
 a) 2.15×3.8 **b)** 21.5×0.38 **c)** $8.17 \div 0.38$

19 Given that $518 \times 74 = 38\,332$, work out the values of
 a) 51.8×7.4 **b)** 0.518×7.4 **c)** $383.32 \div 7.4$

20 Use the fact that $306 \div 17 = 18$ to work out:
 a) 18×1.7 **b)** $306 \div 0.17$ **c)** 1.8×0.17

 EXERCISE 2.3

Write these terminating decimals as exact fractions. Give each answer in its simplest form.

1 0.36 **2** 0.05 **3** 0.7 **4** 0.76 **5** 0.0375

6 0.55 **7** 2.47 **8** 3.33 **9** 0.65 **10** 1.102

Write these recurring decimals as exact fractions, in their simplest form. Show your method clearly.

11 0.$\dot{6}$ **12** 0.3$\dot{7}$ **13** 5.$\dot{1}$ **14** 0.4$\dot{5}\dot{2}$

15 0.1$\dot{3}\dot{4}$ **16** 7.$\dot{3}$ **17** 0.2$\dot{4}$ **18** 6.3$\dot{9}\dot{6}$

Write these fractions as decimals.

19 $\frac{3}{5}$ **20** $\frac{7}{11}$ **21** $\frac{5}{9}$ **22** $\frac{13}{30}$

23 Which is larger: 5.0$\dot{6}\dot{9}$ or 5.1?

24 Aaron says, '2.$\dot{5}$ is exactly twice as big as 1.2$\dot{5}$'.
Is Aaron right or wrong? Explain your answer carefully.

 EXERCISE 2.4

Round these whole numbers to the indicated level of accuracy.

1 856 (to the nearest 10)   **2** 82 135 (to the nearest 100)   **3** 3495 (to the nearest 1000)

4 2789 (to the nearest 10)   **5** 1675 (to the nearest 100)

Round the following decimal numbers to the indicated number of decimal places.

6 5.518 49 (3 d.p.)   **7** 26.0372 (2 d.p.)   **8** 9.751 (1 d.p.)   **9** 1.289 74 (4 d.p.)

10 83.666 (2 d.p.)   **11** 52.40 (1 d.p.)   **12** 9.340 071 1 (4 d.p.)   **13** 0.3498 (3 d.p.)

Round the following to the specified number of significant figures.

14 67.07 (3 s.f.)   **15** 25.32 (1 s.f.)   **16** 183 (2 s.f.)   **17** 78.984 91 (4 s.f.)

18 9134 (2 s.f.)   **19** 18.4 (1 s.f.)   **20** 0.056 17 (3 s.f.)   **21** 129.51 (2 s.f.)

22 The lengths of pieces of wood are measured as 27 cm, to the nearest cm.
Five pieces of wood are placed in a straight line. Work out the smallest possible **total** length.

23 A rectangle has length 57 mm and width 8 mm, both correct to the nearest mm. Work out the largest possible area it could have, giving your answer correct to 3 significant figures.

24 Last week, the number attending the local rugby match was 6400, correct to the nearest hundred. The week before it was 6350, correct to the nearest ten.
Is it possible that the same number of people attended in both weeks? Explain your answer.

25 Write down: **(i)** the maximum possible length **(ii)** the minimum possible length of each of the following lengths, measured to 2 significant figures.
     a) 57 m   **b)** 820 cm   **c)** 3.4 km   **d)** 3800 mm

EXERCISE 2.5 **1** **2**

Write these fractions in their simplest terms.

1 $\frac{12}{48}$ **2** $\frac{24}{72}$ **3** $\frac{8}{20}$ **4** $\frac{22}{77}$ **5** $\frac{5}{35}$

Find the value represented by the symbol * in each of these statements.

6 $\frac{3}{4} = \frac{*}{16}$ **7** $\frac{5}{7} = \frac{15}{*}$ **8** $\frac{28}{35} = \frac{*}{5}$ **9** $\frac{30}{36} = \frac{5}{*}$ **10** $\frac{9}{10} = \frac{*}{40}$

Work out the answers to these without using a calculator.

11 $\frac{1}{5} + \frac{1}{2}$ **12** $\frac{3}{8} - \frac{1}{3}$ **13** $\frac{1}{4} + \frac{3}{7}$ **14** $\frac{5}{6} - \frac{2}{3}$ **15** $\frac{1}{6} + \frac{2}{5}$ **16** $\frac{3}{5} + \frac{1}{4}$

17 $\frac{5}{7} - \frac{1}{3}$ **18** $\frac{2}{5} + \frac{2}{3}$ **19** $\frac{3}{7} - \frac{2}{5}$ **20** $\frac{5}{8} - \frac{1}{3}$ **21** $\frac{11}{12} - \frac{3}{8}$ **22** $\frac{5}{14} + \frac{2}{7}$

23 $\frac{3}{5} - \frac{1}{4}$ **24** $2\frac{1}{4} + 3\frac{2}{3}$ **25** $7\frac{5}{7} - 4\frac{1}{3}$ **26** $\frac{2}{5} + \frac{3}{8}$ **27** $\frac{7}{30} + \frac{7}{20}$ **28** $\frac{5}{9} - \frac{1}{6}$

Use pencil and paper to work out the answer to each of these. Then use your calculator fraction key to check your answers.

29 $1\frac{2}{3} + 3\frac{5}{7}$ **30** $2\frac{3}{4} + 1\frac{5}{9}$ **31** $4\frac{1}{5} - 2\frac{3}{4}$ **32** $5\frac{3}{10} - 3\frac{5}{6}$

33 $10\frac{7}{9} + 6\frac{5}{6}$ **34** $3\frac{2}{7} - 1\frac{3}{5}$ **35** $5\frac{1}{6} - 2\frac{3}{8}$

EXERCISE 2.6

Work out these multiplications and divisions. Show all your working clearly.

1 $\frac{3}{4} \times \frac{2}{5}$ **2** $\frac{2}{3} \times \frac{5}{7}$ **3** $\frac{2}{7} \times \frac{5}{8}$ **4** $\frac{4}{9} \times \frac{15}{22}$ **5** $\frac{7}{8} \times 24$

6 $\frac{3}{11} \times \frac{7}{9}$ **7** $\frac{3}{10} \times \frac{5}{6}$ **8** $35 \times \frac{3}{5}$ **9** $\frac{3}{7} \div \frac{9}{10}$ **10** $\frac{3}{5} \div \frac{6}{7}$

11 $\frac{5}{6} \div \frac{8}{9}$ **12** $\frac{5}{8} \div 40$ **13** $\frac{2}{3} \div \frac{8}{11}$ **14** $36 \div \frac{4}{5}$ **15** $\frac{1}{5} \div \frac{1}{20}$

16 $\frac{8}{9} \div \frac{18}{19}$ **17** $\frac{6}{35} \times \frac{14}{15}$ **18** $\frac{3}{11} \div \frac{3}{11}$ **19** $\frac{5}{7} \times \frac{14}{15}$ **20** $\frac{1}{5} \times \frac{5}{6} \div \frac{1}{3}$

Work out the answers to these calculations. Remember to convert mixed fractions into top-heavy fractions before doing the multiplications or divisions.

21 $5\frac{3}{7} \times 1\frac{9}{19}$ **22** $4\frac{1}{6} \times \frac{4}{15}$ **23** $1\frac{5}{6} \times 1\frac{3}{11}$ **24** $2\frac{2}{7} \times 1\frac{11}{24}$ **25** $1\frac{3}{4} \div 2\frac{1}{7}$

26 $\frac{14}{15} \div 1\frac{2}{5}$ **27** $3\frac{1}{5} \div 2\frac{2}{3}$ **28** $5 \div 2\frac{2}{3}$ **29** $2\frac{1}{2} \div 1\frac{2}{3}$ **30** $2\frac{3}{4} \times 5\frac{1}{3}$

Use pencil and paper to work out the answer to each of these. Then use your calculator fraction key to check your answers.

31 $\frac{12}{25} \times 1\frac{2}{3}$ **32** $6\frac{2}{3} \times 1\frac{1}{5}$ **33** $3\frac{3}{8} \div 2\frac{1}{4}$ **34** $25 \div 1\frac{3}{7}$

35 $33\frac{1}{3} \times \frac{9}{20}$ **36** $2\frac{6}{11} \div 2\frac{7}{22}$

U2 CHAPTER 3

Percentages

All the Exercises in this Chapter are Stage 2 only.

 X EXERCISE 3.1 **2**

Write these percentages as fractions in their simplest form.

1 65%	**2** 90%	**3** 36%	**4** $7\frac{1}{2}$%
5 12%	**6** 340%	**7** 12.5%	**8** $66\frac{2}{3}$%

Express these fractions as percentages. You should do them by hand first.
Then use your calculator's fraction key to check each one.

9 $\frac{28}{50}$ **10** $\frac{15}{20}$ **11** $\frac{57}{60}$ **12** $\frac{12}{30}$ **13** $\frac{24}{60}$ **14** $\frac{22}{55}$ **15** $\frac{12}{40}$ **16** $\frac{36}{80}$

17 Arrange these quantities in order of size, smallest first.

$$0.42, \quad \frac{4}{11}, \quad 45\%, \quad \frac{3}{7}, \quad 0.4, \quad 41\%$$

18 Harry buys a book for £40 and sells it for £32.
   a) How much money has he lost?
   b) What is his percentage loss?

19

Steve's Sausages	Bertie's Bangers
72% beef	44 g out of every 60 g beef

Rob wants to buy the sausages that contain the most beef.
Which sausages should he buy? Explain why.

20 Maria buys a house for £240 000 and sells it three years later for £300 000.
What is her percentage profit?

 EXERCISE 3.2 **2**

1 Find 9% of 500.	**2** Find 20% of 550.	**3** Find 58% of 200.
4 Find 72% of 2400.	**5** Find 44% of £370.	**6** Find 8% of 290 kg.
7 Find 65% of 820 cm.	**8** Find 35% of 60 litres.	

9 A History test was marked out of 75. Melissa scored 84%.
How many marks did Melissa get in the History test?

10 There are 2000 students at Central School. 47% of the students are girls.
   a) Work out the number of girls at Central School.

   15% of the girls walk to school.
   b) Work out the number of girls that walk to school.

U2 CHAPTER 4

Powers, roots and reciprocals

All Exercises are Stage 2. Exercise 4.1 Q1 to Q20 is also Stage 1.

EXERCISE 4.1

Write down the values of the following, without using a calculator.

1 3^2	**2** 5^3	**3** 6^2	**4** 1^3
5 8^2	**6** 6^3	**7** 10^2	**8** 0^3
9 $\sqrt{25}$	**10** $\sqrt{100}$	**11** $\sqrt[3]{8}$	**12** $\sqrt{4}$
13 $\sqrt{121}$	**14** $\sqrt[3]{27}$	**15** $\sqrt{49}$	**16** $\sqrt[3]{1}$

Use your calculator to work out the values of the following expressions.
Round your answers to 3 significant figures where appropriate.

17 21^2	**18** 3.7^2	**19** 12.9^2	**20** 8^3
21 11.4^3	**22** 2.6^3	**23** $\sqrt{20}$	**24** $\sqrt[3]{500}$
25 $\sqrt[3]{26.1}$	**26** $\sqrt{47.3}$	**27** $\sqrt{7.18}$	**28** $\sqrt[3]{1.9}$

29 Find x if $x^2 = 250$. Give your answer to 3 significant figures.

30 Find y if $y^3 = 250$. Give your answer to 2 significant figures.

EXERCISE 4.2

Without using a calculator, find the exact values of these:

1 2^6	**2** $27^{\frac{1}{3}}$	**3** 5^3	**4** $100^{\frac{1}{2}}$
5 2^3	**6** 4^4	**7** $8000^{\frac{1}{3}}$	**8** $900^{\frac{1}{2}}$
9 3^5	**10** $0.0001^{\frac{1}{4}}$	**11** 6^3	**12** $32^{\frac{1}{5}}$

Use your calculator to find the value of each expression. Round your answers as indicated.

13 8^5 (3 s.f.)	**14** 7.2^3 (4 s.f.)	**15** 1.4^6 (2 d.p.)	**16** 0.53^4 (4 d.p.)
17 $18^{\frac{1}{4}}$ (3 s.f.)	**18** $51^{\frac{1}{2}}$ (3 s.f.)	**19** $1752^{\frac{1}{5}}$ (3 d.p.)	**20** $0.923^{\frac{1}{3}}$ (3 s.f.)

EXERCISE 4.3 **2**

Without using a calculator, write the following expressions as simply as possible.

1 $9^{\frac{3}{2}}$ **2** $125^{\frac{2}{3}}$ **3** $32^{\frac{3}{5}}$ **4** $1000^{\frac{4}{3}}$

5 $1^{\frac{8}{3}}$ **6** $64^{\frac{1}{2}}$ **7** $16^{\frac{7}{4}}$ **8** $0.008^{\frac{2}{3}}$

9 $27^{\frac{4}{3}}$ **10** $4^{\frac{5}{2}}$ **11** $100^{\frac{3}{2}}$ **12** $216^{\frac{2}{3}}$

 EXERCISE 4.4 **pt** **2**

Work out the values of these, leaving your answers as exact fractions.

1 2^{-3} **2** 7^{-2} **3** 1^{-6} **4** 3^{-4} **5** 5^{-3}

6 10^{-2} **7** 8^{-1} **8** 4^{-3} **9** 9^{-1} **10** 30^{-2}

Evaluate these expressions, giving your answers as exact fractions.

11 $\left(\frac{8}{7}\right)^{-1}$ **12** $\left(\frac{10}{17}\right)^{-1}$ **13** $\left(\frac{3}{2}\right)^{-3}$ **14** $\left(\frac{5}{6}\right)^{-2}$ **15** $\left(\frac{1}{3}\right)^{-4}$

16 $\left(\frac{81}{49}\right)^{-\frac{1}{2}}$ **17** $\left(\frac{4}{11}\right)^{-1}$ **18** $\left(\frac{1000}{27}\right)^{-\frac{1}{3}}$ **19** $\left(\frac{64}{125}\right)^{-\frac{2}{3}}$ **20** $\left(\frac{16}{9}\right)^{-\frac{3}{2}}$

 EXERCISE 4.5 **2**

Simplify each of these expressions, giving your answer as a number to a single power.

1 $7^5 \times 7^9$ **2** $2^{10} \times 2^6$ **3** $10^8 \div 10^2$ **4** $5^{18} \div 5^6$

5 $8^0 \times 8^5$ **6** $9^9 \times 9$ **7** $15^{80} \div 15^0$ **8** $37^{14} \div 37^7$

9 $(2.6^3)^5$ **10** $58^{\frac{7}{2}} \times 58^{\frac{3}{2}}$ **11** $\dfrac{6^{15}}{6^3}$ **12** $\dfrac{9^{\frac{5}{3}}}{9^{\frac{2}{3}}}$

Work out each of these, giving your answer as an ordinary number.

13 $3^3 \times 3$ **14** $7^5 \div 7^3$ **15** $9^9 \div 9^8$ **16** 5×5^2

17 $4^0 \times 4^3$ **18** $2^8 \div 2^2$ **19** $(2^3)^4$ **20** $8^4 \div 8^2$

21 $(6^5)^0$ **22** $(3^2)^2$ **23** $1^8 \times 1^3$ **24** $(10^3)^2$

EXERCISE 4.6

Write these numbers in standard index form.

1 276 000   **2** 1280   **3** 73 000   **4** 9 000 000   **5** 0.072

6 0.004 63   **7** 0.61   **8** 75.2   **9** 287.03   **10** 0.000 01

Write these as ordinary numbers.

11 7.2×10^4 **12** 3.91×10^3 **13** 6×10^{-2} **14** 4.05×10^{-1} **15** 5.73×10^5

16 8.2×10^{-4} **17** 9.987×10^2 **18** 1.04×10^{-3} **19** 2×10^{-5} **20** 6.7673×10^4

EXERCISE 4.7

Work out the answers to these calculations without using a calculator.
Give your answers in standard form.

1 $(2 \times 10^4) + (5 \times 10^3)$ **2** $(3.9 \times 10^2) + (2.7 \times 10^4)$

3 $(8 \times 10^5) - (8 \times 10^4)$ **4** $(2 \times 10^6) - (5 \times 10^7)$

5 $(3.6 \times 10^{12}) \times (2 \times 10^4)$ **6** $(5 \times 10^9) \times (7 \times 10^{-5})$

7 $(42 \times 10^{15}) \div (6 \times 10^7)$ **8** $(4 \times 10^3) \div (8 \times 10^{-6})$

Use your calculator to evaluate these expressions.
Give your answers in standard form, correct to 3 significant figures.

9 The mass of a neutron is 1.675×10^{-24} grams.
Work out the mass of 8.5×10^{14} neutrons.

10 $(7.13 \times 10^{10}) \times (3.28 \times 10^3)$ **11** $\dfrac{(7.4 \times 10^6) + (1.82 \times 10^7)}{(4.56 \times 10^9)}$

12 $0.0472 \div (5.3 \times 10^{-8})$ **13** $(2.6 \times 10^3)^3$

14 $\dfrac{(5.1 \times 10^{-2}) - (3.4 \times 10^{-1})}{(9.76 \times 10^{-7})}$ **15** $(3.6 \times 10^{12}) \div (2 \times 10^4)$

U2 CHAPTER 5

Working with algebra

All Exercises are Stage 2. Exercises 5.1 to 5.7 are also Stage 1.

EXERCISE 5.1 ① ②

1 If $c = 5$, $h = 7$ and $n = 3$, find the value of:

   a) $2h - 3n$ **b)** $c^2 - 5n$ **c)** $ch - 2hn$ **d)** $(3c - 2h)^2$

2 The final velocity, v, of a particle is found using the formula $v = u + at$
where u is the initial velocity, t is the time and a is the acceleration.

   a) Use your calculator to work out the value of v when $a = 9.8$, $t = 3.57$ and $u = 2.43$.
      Write your answer correct to 3 significant figures.

   b) Find the value of a when $v = 29$, $u = 5$ and $t = 4$.

EXERCISE 5.2 ① ②

Write these expressions using indices.

1 $x \times x \times x \times x$ **2** $y \times y \times y$ **3** $c \times c$

4 $t \times t \times t \times t \times t$ **5** $3 \times h \times h \times h \times h$ **6** $7 \times t \times t$

EXERCISE 5.3 ① ②

Expand and simplify.

1 $3(x + 7) + 4(x + 1)$ **2** $8(x + 2) + 5(x - 2)$ **3** $9(x + 1) + 5(x + 2)$

4 $6(5x - 2) + 9(2x + 3)$ **5** $8(3x + 2) + 2(4x + 3)$ **6** $5(3x + 2) + 4(3x - 2)$

7 $6(x + 6) + 7(3x + 7)$ **8** $7(x - 1) + 4(2x - 1)$ **9** $4(3x + 2) + 5(2x + 3)$

10 $9(8x - 2) + 3(3x + 4)$

Expand and simplify.
Take special care when there is a negative number in front of the second bracket.

11 $5(6x - 1) + 8(2x - 5)$ **12** $2(6x + 5) - (8x + 9)$ **13** $7(x + 9) + 3(x + 2)$

14 $4(4x + 3) - 2(x - 8)$ **15** $3(5x + 7) - 2(3x + 5)$ **16** $8(x + 2) + 5(x - 7)$

17 $9(3x - 4) - 9(2x - 7)$ **18** $6(x - 1) - 4(5x + 2)$ **19** $10(x + 1) + 7(8x - 1)$

20 $11x - 6(3x - 7) + 5x$

EXERCISE 5.4

Expand and simplify.

1 $(x + 1)(5x + 3)$ **2** $(6x + 5)(x + 2)$ **3** $(x + 7)(x + 9)$ **4** $(3x + 2)(2x - 3)$

5 $(x - 5)(4x + 1)$ **6** $(5x - 3)(6x - 1)$ **7** $(9x - 2)(3x + 2)$ **8** $(2x - 9)(5x - 1)$

9 $(4x + 3)(7x - 2)$ **10** $(x + 10)(8x - 3)$ **11** $(7x - 1)(x - 6)$ **12** $(8x + 5)(2x - 5)$

13 $(6x - 11)(3x - 1)$ **14** $(x - 8)(x - 4)$ **15** $(3x + 7)(3x - 7)$ **16** $(x - 9)(x + 8)$

17 $(x - 5)(x + 5)$ **18** $(5x - 1)(5x + 1)$ **19** $(x - 1)^2$ **20** $(2x + 7)^2$

EXERCISE 5.5

Factorise these expressions. They may all be done using the common factor method.

1 $x^2 - 3x$ **2** $3x^2 - 15x$ **3** $6x^2 + 4x$ **4** $y^2 + 7y$

5 $3y^2 - 15y$ **6** $8x + 12x^2$ **7** $20y^2 - 12y$ **8** $20y^2 - 12$

9 $5fg + g^2$ **10** $6y^2 - 8y$ **11** $3x^3 - 2x^2$ **12** $12x^8 + 14x^7$

13 $8ab - 27b^2$ **14** $10y - 25$ **15** $6y + 3xy$ **16** $21x^2y + 14xy^2$

17 $24y^3 - 16y^2$ **18** $14y - 7y^3$ **19** $9x^2 + 3$ **20** $4p^2q - 6pq^2 + 8pq$

EXERCISE 5.6

Factorise these quadratic expressions.

1 $x^2 + 5x + 4$ **2** $x^2 + 15x + 14$ **3** $x^2 + 8x + 15$ **4** $x^2 + 10x + 21$

5 $x^2 + 7x + 12$ **6** $x^2 - 2x + 1$ **7** $x^2 - 9x + 14$ **8** $x^2 - 12x + 27$

9 $x^2 - 14x + 40$ **10** $x^2 - 9x + 18$ **11** $x^2 + 5x - 14$ **12** $x^2 - x - 20$

13 $x^2 - 5x - 24$ **14** $x^2 + 3x - 10$ **15** $x^2 - 11x + 18$ **16** $x^2 + 10x + 24$

17 $x^2 + 4x - 12$ **18** $x^2 - 8x - 20$ **19** $x^2 - 13x + 22$ **20** $x^2 - 2x - 35$

EXERCISE 5.7

Factorise these quadratic expressions.

1 $2x^2 + 11x + 5$ **2** $3x^2 + 5x + 2$ **3** $2x^2 + 9x + 7$ **4** $5x^2 + 7x + 2$

5 $7x^2 + 13x - 2$ **6** $3x^2 - 2x - 5$ **7** $5x^2 + 4x - 1$ **8** $7x^2 - 5x - 2$

9 $2x^2 - 7x + 6$ **10** $3x^2 + 8x - 3$ **11** $2x^2 - 9x + 10$ **12** $8x^2 - 14x + 3$

13 $6x^2 + 11x + 4$ **14** $6x^2 - 17x + 5$ **15** $3x^2 + 17x + 10$ **16** $9x^2 - 12x + 4$

17 $8x^2 + 10x - 3$ **18** $10x^2 - 13x - 3$ **19** $12x^2 + 11x + 2$ **20** $7x^2 - 18x - 9$

 EXERCISE 5.8A **2**

Factorise these expressions, using the difference of two squares method.

1 $x^2 - 9$ **2** $x^2 - 100$ **3** $y^2 - 25$ **4** $x^2 - 900$ **5** $2y^2 - 2$

6 $5x^2 - 20$ **7** $3x^2 - 300$ **8** $2y^2 - 72$ **9** $7y^2 - 28$ **10** $10x^2 - 490$

 EXERCISE 5.8B **2**

This exercise contains a mixture of all the different factorising methods you have learnt so far.
Factorise these expressions.

1 $x^2 - 5x$ **2** $y^2 + 7y + 10$ **3** $x^2 - 64$ **4** $x^2 - 10x + 16$

5 $y^2 + 3y - 28$ **6** $5x^2 - 15x$ **7** $2x^2 - 11x + 14$ **8** $y^2 - 81$

9 $y^2 - 5y - 50$ **10** $x^2 - 9x - 10$ **11** $x^2 + 16x$ **12** $12x^2 + 4x - 1$

13 $7xy - 21y^2$ **14** $2y^2 - 5y + 2$ **15** $y^2 + y - 30$ **16** $2x^2 - 50$

17 $x^2 - 9x + 18$ **18** $6y^2 + 9y$ **19** $3x^2 - 20x - 7$ **20** $5y^2 - 125$

 EXERCISE 5.9 **2**

Express each of these as a single fraction.

1 $\dfrac{x}{2} + \dfrac{x+4}{3}$ **2** $\dfrac{x-2}{3} + \dfrac{x+5}{4}$ **3** $\dfrac{2x}{7} + \dfrac{x+3}{5}$

4 $\dfrac{x+3}{2} - \dfrac{x+1}{5}$ **5** $\dfrac{5x+3}{4} + \dfrac{x}{7}$ **6** $\dfrac{3x-1}{5} + \dfrac{x-2}{2}$

7 $\dfrac{6}{x} + \dfrac{5}{x-2}$ **8** $\dfrac{1}{x-4} + \dfrac{3}{x-2}$ **9** $\dfrac{5}{x-2} + \dfrac{3}{x+3}$

10 $\dfrac{4}{x+5} + \dfrac{3}{x+2}$

Simplify these algebraic fractions.

11 $\dfrac{3x - 9}{6x + 3}$ **12** $\dfrac{30 - 10x}{5x + 15}$ **13** $\dfrac{6x^2 + 9x}{3x}$ **14** $\dfrac{(2x - 1)^7}{(2x - 1)^5}$

15 $\dfrac{x^2 - 2x}{3x}$ **16** $\dfrac{x^2 + 4x}{x^2 - 3x}$ **17** $\dfrac{x^2 + 8x}{2x^2 + 4x}$

Simplify fully these expressions.

18 $\dfrac{x^2 + 6x + 5}{x + 5}$ **19** $\dfrac{x^2 + x - 12}{x^2 - 16}$ **20** $\dfrac{x^2 + 5x - 14}{x^2 + 4x - 21}$

EXERCISE 5.10 ②

1 Write down expressions for the following:
    a) 3 more than x **b)** 8 more than w
    c) 5 less than v **d)** 23 multiplied by c
    e) r lots of 4   **f)** r squared
    g) $5a$ more than $3b$ **h)** 23 divided by d
    i) the sum of g and $2h$ **j)** p divided by q
    k) $3e$ all squared   **l)** t divided by u
    m) 5 lots of f squared   **n)** c squared multiplied by n cubed

2 Kevin has k sweets.
    Julie has 5 more sweets than Kevin.
    a) Write down an expression, in terms of k, for the number of sweets that Julie has.

    Peter has 8 more sweets than Julie.
    b) Write down an expression, in terms of k, for the number of sweets that Peter has.

    Joe has 3 times as many sweets as Peter.
    c) Write down an expression, in terms of k, for the number of sweets that Joe has.
    d) Kevin has 17 sweets. How many sweets does Joe have?

3 The base of a parallelogram is 7 cm more than its height, h.
    a) Write down an expression, in terms of h, for the base of the parallelogram.
    b) Write down an expression, in terms of h, for the area of the parallelogram.
    c) Work out the area of parallelogram when:
        (i) $h = 5$ cm   **(ii)** $h = 1$ cm   **(iii)** $h = 4$ cm

> Remember that the area of a parallelogram is base × height

4 a) Write down an expression for the area of this square.

□ x cm

    Nine of these squares are put together to make a large square.

    b) Write down an expression for the area of the large square.
    c) What is the length of one side of the large square?
    d) Explain how this shows that $9x^2 = (3x)^2$.

5 Pens cost x pence each.
Pencils cost y pence each.

Write down an expression for the cost in pence of:
a) 3 pens
b) 8 pencils
c) 5 pens and 6 pencils
d) n pens

6 Pears cost p pence each.
Apricots cost a pence each.

Write down an expression for the cost in pence of:
a) 2 pears
b) 7 apricots
c) 8 pears and 1 apricot

7 A small bottle of cola costs c pence.
A large bottle of cola costs three times as much as the small bottle of cola.

Write down an expression for the cost in pence of:
a) a large bottle of cola
b) 8 large bottles of cola
c) 2 small bottles of cola and 5 large bottles of cola.

U2 CHAPTER 6

Coordinates and straight-line graphs

All Exercises are Stage 2. Exercises 6.1, 6.3 and 6.4 are also Stage 1.

EXERCISE 6.1

1 Using the diagram, write down the coordinates of A, B, C, D and E.

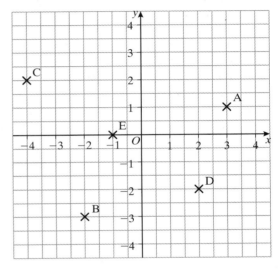

2 The questions refer to the diagram.
   a) Which point is at $(-4, -2)$?
   b) What are the coordinates of L?
   c) Which point is midway between $(2, -6)$ and $(8, 0)$?
   d) What are the coordinates of H?
   e) Which point has the largest y coordinate?
   f) Which point has the smallest x coordinate?
   g) Which point has the same x coordinate and y coordinate?

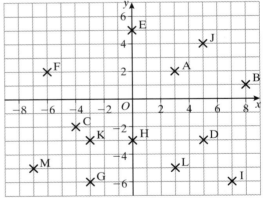

3 Follow these instructions carefully.
   Draw a coordinate grid and label both axes from -10 to 10 on the x axis and -4 to 4 on the y axis.
   Now draw line segments as follows:
   a) From $(-8, 3)$ to $(-8, -3)$ **b)** From $(-2, 3)$ to $(-2, -3)$ **d)** From $(6, 3)$ to $(6, -3)$
   From $(-8, 0)$ to $(-5, 3)$ **c)** From $(0, 3)$ to $(4, 3)$ From $(6, 3)$ to $(9, 3)$
   From $(-8, 0)$ to $(-5, -3)$ From $(2, 3)$ to $(2, -3)$ From $(6, 0)$ to $(8, 0)$
   From $(6, -3)$ to $(9, -3)$

   You should find that you have named a 4-sided shape.
   Draw a sketch of this shape.

4 Here is a puzzle using a coordinate grid.
Draw a coordinate grid so that x and y both run from -6 to 6.
  a) Draw three squares in the following positions:
    Join $(2, 2)$ to $(-1, 2)$ to $(-1, -1)$ to $(2, -1)$ to $(2, 2)$.
    Join $(-1, 2)$ to $(-4, 2)$ to $(-4, 5)$ to $(-1, 5)$ to $(-1, 2)$.
    Join $(2, -1)$ to $(5, -1)$ to $(5, -4)$ to $(2, -4)$ to $(2, -1)$.
    You should now have three squares.
  b) To solve the puzzle move exactly four of the lines so that there are exactly five squares.

EXERCISE 6.2 **2**

For questions **1** to **8** you are given a linear function and an incomplete table of values.

Work out the missing values to complete the table, and then plot the graph of the corresponding line segment. You may use either graph paper or squared paper.

1 $y = 3x + 1$

x	-2	0	1
y	-5	1	

2 $y = 4x$

x	-1	0	2
y	-4		

3 $y = 3x - 2$

x	-1	0	2
y			

4 $y = 4 - x$

x	-2	0	2
y			

5 $x + y = 5$

x	-5	0	5
y			

6 $y = \frac{1}{2}x + 2$

x			
y			

7 $y = 2x - 1$

x			
y			

8 $2x + 3y = 6$

x			
y			

9 Draw up a set of coordinate axes so that x runs from -3 to 3 and y from -10 to 10.
  a) Calculate the coordinates of three points that lie on the line $y = 3x + 2$.
    Hence plot the line $y = 3x + 2$ on your coordinate axes.
  b) Now calculate the coordinates of three points that lie on the line $y = 3x - 2$.
    Plot the line $y = 3x - 2$ on the same set of coordinate axes.
  c) Look at your two graphs. What do you notice?

10 Draw up a set of coordinate axes so that x runs from -6 to 6 and y from 0 to 12.
  a) Calculate the coordinates of three points that lie on the line $y = 6 - x$.
    Hence plot the line $y = 6 - x$ on your coordinate axes.
  b) Now calculate the coordinates of three points that lie on the line $y = 6 + x$.
    Plot the line $y = 6 + x$ on the same set of coordinate axes.
  c) Look at your two graphs. What do you notice?

EXERCISE 6.3

Find the coordinates of the midpoint of the line segment between these points.

1 A(7, 3) and B(3, 11)

2 C(9, 0) and D(1, 8)

3 E(2, −5) and F(6, 3)

4 G(−1, 4) and H(−3, 10)

5 I(6, 6) and J(−2, 2)

6 K(0, 7) and L(−8, 9)

7 M(−6, −11) and N(0, −4)

8 P(6, −10) and Q(−3, 5)

EXERCISE 6.4

1 The diagram shows a cuboid ABCDOEFG.
E has coordinates (2, 0, 0). B has coordinates (2, 4, 3).

 a) Write down the coordinates of the points A, C, D, F and G.

 b) The point M is midway between O and B. Find the coordinates of M.

 c) The point N is midway between B and D. Find the coordinates of N.

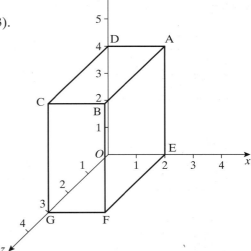

2 The diagram shows a solid OABC.
PA and QC are parallel to the x axis,
BC is parallel to the y axis, BA is parallel to the z axis.
OB = 7 units, OQ = 6 units, OP = 3 units.

 a) Write down the coordinates of A, B and C.

 M is the midpoint of BC,
 and N is the midpoint of AC.

 b) Find the coordinates of M and N.

 c) Use your answers to part **b)** to explain how you can tell the line segment MN is horizontal.

 d) What name best describes the solid OABC?

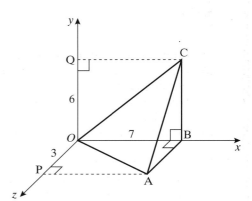

3 The diagram shows a cuboid ABCDEFGO.
E is (5, 0, 0), D is (0, 3, 0), G is (0, 0, 2).

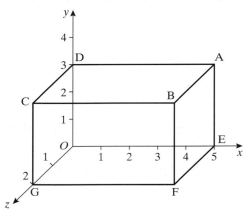

    a) Write down the coordinates of B and C.

M is the midpoint of BD.
    b) Find the coordinates of M.

N is the midpoint of EG.
    c) Find the coordinates of N.
    d) **(i)** Write down the coordinates of the
           midpoint of MN.
      (ii) Explain how you could get these coordinates
           without working out the coordinates of M
           and N.

4 Point A is at (2, 3, 0), B is at (4, 11, 6) and C is at (4, 9, 6).
M is the midpoint of line segment AB.
    a) Work out the coordinates of the point M.

N is the midpoint of line segment MC.
    b) Work out the coordinates of the point N.

5 Here are the coordinates of six points:
    A (1, 3, 0),   B (5, 2, 0),   C (1, 5, 0),   D (3, 4, 0),   E (4, 3, 0),   F (2, 0, 3).
    a) Which of the points is the midpoint of the line segment BD?
    b) What can you say about the triangle ACD?

U2 CHAPTER 7

Number sequences

All Exercises in this Chapter are Stage 1.

EXERCISE 7.1 **1**

In questions **1** to **8**, write down the next two terms in each of the number sequences, and explain how each term is worked out. Give an expression for the nth term in each case.

They are all related to the list of common sequences in the table on page 92 of your textbook.

1 5, 8, 11, 14, 17...

2 4, 9, 14, 19, 24...

3 13, 23, 33, 43, 53...

4 5, 12, 19, 26, 33...

5 0, 3, 8, 15, 24, 35...

6 11, 101, 1001, 10 001, 100 001...

7 2, 8, 18, 32, 50, 72...

8 3, 10, 29, 66, 127, 218...

9 Look at this pattern of trapeziums made from matchsticks.

Pattern 1   Pattern 2   Pattern 3

a) How many matchsticks would there be in pattern 7?
b) Find a formula for the number of matchsticks, S, in pattern n.

10 Look at this pattern of spots in rectangles.

   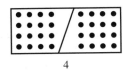

1   2   3   4

Number of spots in rectangle:

$1 \times 2 = 2$ $2 \times 4 = 8$ $3 \times 6 = 18$ $4 \times 8 = 32$

Number of spots in half-rectangle:

$$\frac{1 \times 2}{2} = 1 \qquad \frac{2 \times 4}{2} = 4 \qquad \frac{3 \times 6}{2} = 9 \qquad \frac{4 \times 8}{2} = 16$$

a) Find an expression for the number of spots in rectangle n.
b) Find an expression for the number of spots in half-rectangle n.

EXERCISE 7.2 ①

1 A number sequence is defined as follows:
- The first term is 28.
- Each new term is 3 less than the previous one.

Use this rule to generate the first five terms of the number sequence.

2 A number sequence is defined as follows:
- The first term is 6.
- To find each new term, double the previous term, and then subtract 5.

Use this rule to generate the first four terms of the number sequence.

3 The nth term of a number sequence is given by the expression $4n - 3$.
a) Write down the first five terms of the number sequence.
b) Work out the 20th term.

4 The nth term of a number sequence is given by the expression $\frac{1}{2}(10n + 3)$.
a) Write down the first six terms of the number sequence.
b) Work out the 10th term.

5 Andrew writes this sequence of numbers: 11, 15, 19, 23, 27…
a) Describe Andrew's pattern in words.
b) Find the tenth term in Andrew's number sequence.

6 The nth term of a number sequence is given by the expression $60 - 2n$.
a) Write down the first five terms of the number sequence.
b) Work out the 50th term.

7 In a certain number sequence, the first term is 5.
Each new term is found by multiplying the previous term by 5.
a) Write down the first five terms of the number sequence.
b) What name is given to this particular number sequence?

8 The nth term of a number sequence is given by the formula $6n + 1$.
a) Work out the first four terms.
b) Find the 20th term.
c) One of the terms in the sequence is 727. Which term is this?

9 The nth term of a number sequence is given by the expression $\dfrac{(n + 1)(n + 2)}{2}$.
a) Write down the first four terms.
b) Work out the 39th term.
c) Explain why all the terms in this sequence are integers.

10 Dana is working with a number sequence.
The nth term of this sequence is given by the expression $8n - 1$.
Dana gets the number 1846 as one of her terms.
Show that she must have made a mistake.

EXERCISE 7.3

1 The first five terms in an arithmetic sequence are:

8, 14, 20, 26, 32…

a) Find the tenth term.
b) Write down, in terms of n, an expression for the nth term of this sequence.

2 The first four terms in an arithmetic sequence are:

43, 38, 33, 28…

a) Find the first negative term.
b) Write down, in terms of n, an expression for the nth term of this sequence.

Here are some arithmetic sequences.
For each one, find, in terms of n, an expression for the nth term of the sequence.

3 5, 12, 19, 26, 33…

4 20, 16, 12, 8, 4…

5 11, 22, 33, 44, 55…

6 23, 20, 17, 14, 11…

7 51, 41, 31, 21, 11…

8 3, 7, 11, 15, 19…

9 Robert has been making patterns with matchsticks.
Here are his first three patterns.

      Pattern 1   Pattern 2   Pattern 3

a) Work out the number of matchsticks in pattern 6.
b) Give a formula for the number of matchsticks, s, in pattern n.
c) Explain how your formula relates to the way the matchsticks fit together.

10 The seventh term of an arithmetic sequence is 34 and the eighth term is 40.
a) Write down the common difference for this sequence.
b) Work out the first term.
c) Find a formula for the nth term of the sequence.
Check that your formula works when $n = 7$ and $n = 8$.

Working with shape and space

All Exercises are Stage 2. Exercises 8.1, 8.2, 8.3 and 8.4 are also Stage 1.

 EXERCISE 8.1A

Here are some quadrilaterals.

Match each of these words with the shapes A to F.

1 rectangle   **2** square   **3** parallelogram

4 rhombus   **5** kite   **6** trapezium

 EXERCISE 8.1B **1** **2**

Find the values of the angles represented by the letters in each diagram.

1

2

3

4

5

6

7

8

EXERCISE 8.2

1 Find the value of *y*.

2 Find the value of *m*.

3 Find the value of *y*.

4 Find the value of *f*.

5 Find the value of *g*.

6 Two of the angles in a triangle are 34° and 112°.
   a) Work out the size of the third angle.
   b) What kind of triangle is this?

7 The diagram shows an iscoseles triangle.
   Work out the value of *h*.

8 The diagram shows a quadrilateral.
   Work out the value of *g*.

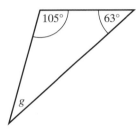

9 Find the size of each angle marked *x*.

10 Find the size of each angle marked *h*.

11 The diagram shows a quadrilateral.
Work out the value of *y*.

EXERCISE 8.3 ❶ ❷

Find the perimeter and the area of each shape. You may use standard formulae to help.

1

3 cm, 5 cm, 4 cm

2

5 m, 12 m, 13 m

3

8 mm, 5.6 mm, 8 mm, 11.4 mm

4

10 cm, 8.66 cm, 10 cm, 10 cm

5

7 cm, 8.5 cm, 10 cm

6

14 cm, 10 cm, 8 cm, 20 cm

7

9 m, 9 m, 7 m, 9 m, 9 m

8

5.6 cm, 4 cm, 3.8 cm, 4 cm, 8.2 cm

8 Working with shape and space U2

Calculate the perimeter and area of each shape. State the units in each case.

9

10

11

12

13

14

15 A quadrilateral has two pairs of parallel sides, but not all angles are the same size. What type of quadrilateral is it?

16 A quadrilateral has all four angles the same size. Daksha says, 'It must be a rectangle.' Is Daksha right? Explain your answer.

17 The diagram shows a rectangle.
   a) Write down an expression, in terms of x, for the perimeter of the rectangle.
   b) If $x = 10$, work out the perimeter of the rectangle.

18 The diagram shows an isosceles triangle. AB = AC. All the lengths are in cm.
   a) Find an expression, in terms of x, for the perimeter of the triangle.
   b) Given that $x = 2$ cm, work out the perimeter of the triangle.

19 The diagram shows a triangle.
   All the lengths are in cm.
   a) What type of triangle is this?
   b) Find an expression, in terms of x, for the
   perimeter of the triangle.

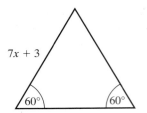

$7x + 3$

$60°$ $60°$

20 The diagram shows a parallelogram.
   All lengths are in metres.

   Write down an expression, in terms of x and y,
   for the perimeter of the parallelogram.

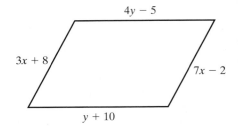

$4y - 5$

$3x + 8$

$7x - 2$

$y + 10$

EXERCISE 8.4 **①** **②**

1 The diagram shows a cube of side 3 m.
   Calculate: **a)** its surface area

   b) its volume.
   State the units in your answers.

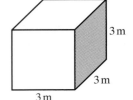

$3\,m$

$3\,m$

$3\,m$

2 The diagram shows a cuboid with
   dimensions 5 cm, 8 cm and 10 cm.
   Calculate: **a)** its surface area **①**

   b) its volume. **②**
   State the units in your answers.

$8\,cm$

$5\,cm$

$10\,cm$

3 The diagram shows a prism.
   Its cross section is formed by a right-angled triangle
   of sides 6 cm, 8 cm and 10 cm.
   The prism has a length of 12 cm.
   a) Calculate the area of the cross section,
   shaded in the diagram.

   b) Work out the volume of the prism.

   c) Calculate the surface area of the prism. **①**

$10\,cm$

$6\,cm$

$12\,cm$

$8\,cm$

4 The cross section of a steel girder is in the shape of a letter T.
The cross section is shown in the diagram.
a) Work out the area of the T-shaped cross section. **1**

The girder is 50 cm long.
b) Work out the volume of the girder. **2**

5 A cube measures 20 cm along each side.
a) Work out the volume of the cube. **2**   **b)** Work out the surface area of the cube. **1**

6 A cuboid measures 37 cm by 40 cm by 5 cm.
a) Work out the volume of the cuboid. **2**   **b)** Work out the surface area of the cuboid. **1**

7 The diagram shows a water tank.
It is in the shape of a cuboid.
It has no lid.
a) Work out the volume of the tank, correct
to 3 significant figures. **2**
b) Work out the total surface area of the
inside of the tank. **1**

8 The diagram shows a sketch of a swimming pool. **2**

The pool is 1 m deep at the shallow end, and 3 m deep at the deep end.
The pool is 25 m long and 8 m wide.
a) Work out the volume of the pool.
1 cubic metre = 1000 litres
b) Work out the number of litres of water in the pool when it is full.

9 A cube has a volume of 1000 cm³. **2**
a) Work out the dimensions of the cube.   **b)** Calculate the surface area of the cube.

10 A cuboid has a volume of 40 cm³. **2**
Its dimensions are all integers bigger than 1.
No two dimensions are the same.
a) Work out the dimensions of the cuboid.   **b)** Calculate the surface area of the cuboid.

U2 CHAPTER 9

Properties of circles

All Exercises in this Chapter are Stage 2.

 EXERCISE 9.1 **2**

1 PT is a tangent to the circle, centre O. Angle POT = 67°.
   a) State, with a reason, the value of the angle marked x.
   b) Work out the value of the angle marked y.

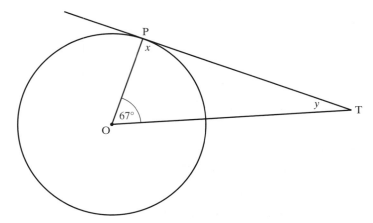

2 PT is a tangent to the circle, centre O.
   PT = 12 cm. OP = 5 cm.
   The line OT intersects the circle at R, as shown.
   Work out the length of RT.

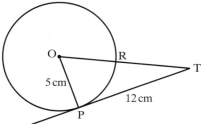

3 TP and TR are tangents to the circle, centre O. Angle POR is 148°.

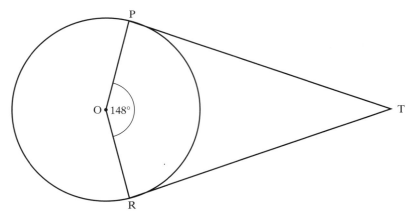

   a) Work out the size of angle PTR. Give reasons.
   b) What type of quadrilateral is OPTR? Explain your reasoning.

4 TP and TR are tangents to the circle, centre O. Angle ORP is 10°.

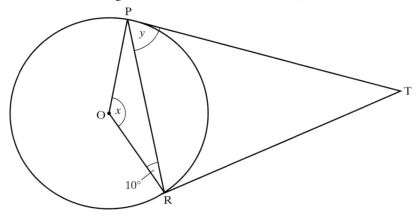

a) Work out the value of x.
b) Work out the value of y.
c) What type of triangle is triangle RPT?

5 AC and BC are tangents to the circle, centre O. Angle ACO = 27°.
The length of the tangent BC is 16 cm.

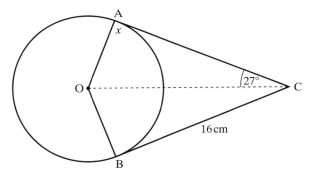

a) Write down the length of the tangent AC.
b) Write down the size of angle OAC, marked x.
c) Work out the size of angle AOB.

EXERCISE 9.2 **2**

1 Follow these instructions to make an accurate drawing of a regular pentagon.

Step 1 Using compasses, construct a circle of radius 6 cm.

Step 2 Using your protractor, draw a sector using an angle of 72°.

72°

Step 4 Complete the construction by joining the five points around the circumference of the circle.

Step 3 Repeat Step 2 to create a full set of 72° sectors.

2 Adapt the instructions from question 1 to make:
   a) a regular hexagon
   b) a regular 10-sided polygon
   c) a 10-pointed star.

3 **a)** Use the rule 'angle at centre = 360° ÷ number of sides' to work out the angle at the centre in order to construct a regular ten-sided polygon (*decagon*) inside a circle.
   b) Use compasses to draw a circle of radius 6 cm.
   c) Using a protractor, construct a regular decagon inside the circle.

4 **a)** Use compasses to make a circle of radius 5 cm.
   b) Using a protractor, construct an equilateral triangle inside the circle.

5 **a)** Use compasses to make a circle of radius 7 cm.
   b) Using a protractor, construct a regular six-sided polygon (*hexagon*) inside the circle.

6 **a)** Use compasses to make two circles of radius 8 cm.
   b) Using a protractor, construct twelve points at equal intervals around the circumference of each circle.
   c) On the first circle, join the points up to make a regular twelve-sided polygon inside the circle.
   d) On the second circle, join the points up in a different way to make a twelve-pointed star.

U2 CHAPTER 10

Working with units

All Exercises in this Chapter are Stage 1.

EXERCISE 10.1

1 Convert 2600 grams into kilograms.

2 Convert 83 000 cm into metres.

3 Write 8.37 km in metres.

4 Express 12.03 litres in ml.

5 Work out how many seconds there are in 30 minutes.

6 A large pot holds 12 litres. A jug holds 200 millilitres of water.
   Work out how many jugs must be used to fill the pot with water.

7 Anju is at school for 450 minutes. Convert this time into hours.

8 Work out the perimeter of this rectangle.
   Give your answer in mm.

   0.7 m ⎡‾‾‾‾‾‾‾‾2.3 m‾‾‾‾‾‾‾‾⎤

9 A box contains 50 packets of biscuits.
   Each packet of biscuits weighs 110 grams.
   Work out the total weight of the 50 packets of biscuits. Give your answer in kilograms.

10 A regular eight-sided shape (*octagon*) has a perimeter of 160 mm.
    Work out the length of one side. Give your answer in cm.

EXERCISE 10.2

1 Suggest a suitable metric unit for measuring the capacity of a teaspoon.

2 Emily weighs 55 kg. What is Emily's weight in pounds?

3 Noah travels 370 miles. What is 370 miles in kilometres?

4 Piero buys 10 litres of milk for his café. How many pints of milk is this?

5 Suggest a sensible Imperial unit to measure the length of a garden.

6 Priya draws a line that is 12 inches long. How long is this line in centimetres?

7 A container contains 20 gallons of oil. How many litres of oil is this?

8 Write down a sensible metric unit that can be used to measure:
   a) the length of a pen   **b)** the weight of a pen.

9 Change 24 km into miles.

10 Julie pays £1.50 for a pound of apples.
    Roughly how much would one kilogram of these apples cost?

EXERCISE 10.3

1   A car travels 50 miles in one hour 15 minutes.
    What is the average speed of the car in miles
    per hour?

2   Martin drives 200 km at an average speed
    of 40 km/h
    How long does the journey take?

3   The density of water is 1000 kg/m³.
    Find the mass of 20 m³ of water.

4   A cyclist travels 10 metres in 3 seconds.
    Work out his speed in km/h.

5   Ian jogs for 40 minutes at an average speed of 80 metres per minute.
    How far does Ian run?

6   Robert runs 100 metres in 20 seconds.
    a)   What is his average speed in metres per second?
    b)   What is Robert's average speed in kilometres per hour?

7   An aluminium hubcap has a volume of 2620 cm³. The mass of the hubcap is 720 g.
    Work out the density of aluminium in g/cm³.

8   Debbie drives 120 km at an average speed of 100 km/h.
    How long in minutes does the journey take?

9   The density of silver is 10.49 g/cm³.
    Give all your answers to 3 significant figures.
    a)   Find the volume of silver used to make a silver ring of mass 35 g.
    b)   Find the volume of silver used to make a silver spoon of mass 200 g.

    A silver coin has a volume of 3 cm³.
    c)   What is the mass of the coin?

10 An intercity train travels at 160 km/h.
    a)   How far does it travel in:
         (i)   30 minutes   (ii)   45 minutes   (iii)   1 hour 15 minutes?
    b)   How long in minutes does it take to travel:
         (i)   80 km   (ii)   8 km   (iii)   200 km?
    c)   What is the speed of the train in metres per second?
         Give your answer correct to 1 decimal place.

11 Geoff went by coach to Bradingham Gardens
    for lunch. The coach went directly to the
    gardens from the coach stop. On the way
    home the coach stopped at a stall.
    The travel graph below shows Geoff's
    journey.

    a)   How long did Geoff spend at
         Bradingham Gardens?
    b)   Work out the speed of the coach, in
         miles per hour, on the
         outward journey.
    c)   Did the coach travel at the same speed
         as this on the **return** journey?

12 Claire leaves her house for school at 7 am each morning.
She walks to the bus stop and waits for her bus.
Here is a distance–time graph for Claire's journey to school.

a) What time does Claire reach the bus stop?
b) How long does she have to wait for the bus?
c) How far away from Claire's house is:
   (i) the bus stop   (ii) the school?
d) What is Claire's average speed, in km per hour, on her journey:
   (i) from A to B   (ii) from C to D?

EXERCISE 10.4

1 Measure the bearings of
each of the following
six towns from Gingbridge.

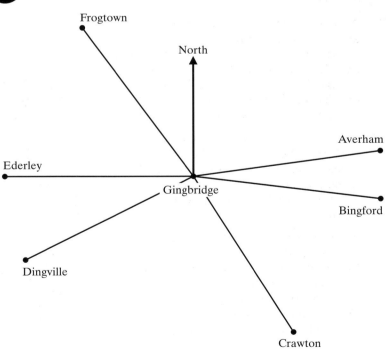

2 A pirate walks on a bearing of 137° from a cave to some buried treasure.
On what bearing should he walk in order to make the return journey to the cave?

3 The diagram shows a lighthouse L and four ships A, B, C and D.

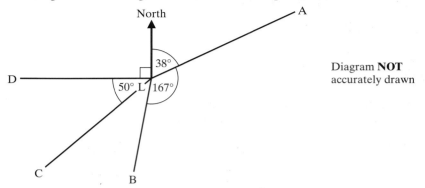

Diagram **NOT**
accurately drawn

Work out the bearing of each of the four ships from the lighthouse.

4 A ship is 10.8 km away from a lighthouse on a bearing of 250°.
a) Make a scale drawing of the ship and the lighthouse. Use a scale of 1 cm to 1 km.

A ferry is 15 km away from the ship on a bearing of 127°.
b) Add the position of the ferry to your scale drawing.
c) Measure the bearing of the ferry from the lighthouse.

5 Look at this sketch. It is not drawn to scale.
a) Write down the bearing of B from A.
b) Work out the bearing of A from B.

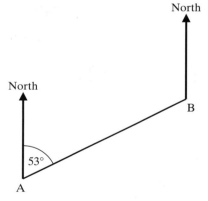

U2 CHAPTER 11

Using a calculator efficiently

All Exercises in this Chapter are Stage 2.

 EXERCISE 11.1

Use your calculator to work out the values of these quantities.
Give your answers correct to 3 significant figures where appropriate.

1 132^2

2 9^4

3 380^6

4 13^5

5 $\sqrt{20}$

6 $\sqrt[3]{83}$

7 $\sqrt[8]{3000}$

8 $\sqrt[3]{71}$

9 23^{-2}

10 3.2^{-1}

11 0.5^{-1}

12 $\frac{2}{7}$

13 $18^{\frac{1}{4}}$

14 $228^{\frac{2}{3}}$

15 $60^{-\frac{3}{4}}$

16 $\sqrt[4]{75}$

17 Find the square of the square of 11.

18 Find the square root of the square root of 163.

19 Find the square root of the cube root of 85.

20 Find the reciprocal of the reciprocal of 27.3.

 EXERCISE 11.2

Use your calculator to work out the values of the following expressions. Write down all the figures on your calculator display, then round the answer to 3 significant figures where appropriate.

1 $(5.2 - 8.7 \times 0.3)^2 \div 6.2$

2 $\sqrt{16.8 \div 2.7 + 18}$

3 $(18.7 - 72.1 \div 5.8)^3$

4 $\dfrac{17.8 \times 0.032}{17.8 - 8.4}$

5 $\dfrac{7.6 \div 1.9^3}{0.31 + 0.2}$

6 $(3.87 + 2.1 \times 4)^{\frac{2}{3}}$

7 $\dfrac{53.5}{18.7 - 6.1 \times 3.9}$

8 $\sqrt{\dfrac{3.7 \times 2.2}{6 + 0.3^2}}$

9 $187 \div (9.03 + \sqrt{20.6})$

10 $17.1 \times (9.8 - 3.7)^2$

11 $\sqrt[3]{3.8^2 - 1.4^2}$

12 $\dfrac{7^3 + 2^2}{6^2 - 4^2}$

13 $\dfrac{22 - 1.82^2}{123 - 10.1^2}$

14 $\sqrt{57.2^2 - 46.1^2}$

15 $\dfrac{18.3 \times 1.1}{8.2 \times 2.8 - 3.1 \times 1.3}$

16 $\dfrac{6.2^2}{3.8^2 + 1.3^2}$

Use your calculator to work out the value of each of the following:

17 $\dfrac{8.7 \times 10^{15} + 9.6 \times 10^{12}}{3.4 \times 10^{7}}$

Give your answer in standard form correct to 3 significant figures.

18 $\sqrt[3]{9.15 \times 10^{28}}$

Give your answer in standard form correct to 2 significant figures.

19 $\dfrac{6.4 \times 10^{17}}{9.32 \times 10^{-3} - 8.15 \times 10^{15}}$

Give your answer in standard form correct to 3 significant figures.

20 $\sqrt{2.19 \times 10^{-4} + 7.83 \times 10^{15}}$

Give your answer in standard form correct to 3 significant figures.

EXERCISE 11.3 **2**

Use your calculator's fraction key to work out the answers to the following calculations.
Give your answers as ordinary fractions or mixed fractions as appropriate.

1 $\frac{3}{8} + \frac{4}{7}$ **2** $\frac{7}{9} \times \frac{5}{11}$ **3** $\frac{3}{4} - \frac{4}{17}$ **4** $\frac{7}{27} \div \frac{5}{6}$ **5** $6\frac{5}{8} + 8\frac{7}{11}$

6 $8\frac{2}{5} - 6\frac{5}{7}$ **7** $3\frac{2}{11} \times 2\frac{3}{5}$ **8** $2\frac{1}{7} \div 1\frac{1}{4}$ **9** $\left(3\frac{2}{9}\right)^2$ **10** $\sqrt{2\frac{7}{9}}$

Use your calculator to find the answers to these calculations as decimals.
Then convert the answers into exact fractions, using your fraction key.

11 6.4×2.6 **12** 0.75×13.2 **13** $51.875 \div 8.3$

14 $\sqrt{6.0025}$ **15** $15.08 - 2.8^2$ **16** $4.5^2 - 2.25$

17 $(13.9 + 17.6) \div 3.6$ **18** $(15^2 + 9^2 + 1^2) \times 0.02$ **19** $\sqrt[4]{133.6336}$

20 $14.85 \div 3.6$

UNIT 3

U3 CHAPTER 12

Fractions, ratios and percentages

EXERCISE 12.1

Work out the following, writing your answer as a fraction in its simplest form.

1 a) $\frac{3}{5} + \frac{1}{4}$ b) $\frac{2}{3} + \frac{1}{8}$ c) $\frac{9}{10} - \frac{3}{5}$ d) $\frac{13}{20} - \frac{1}{3}$

    e) $\frac{5}{6} + \frac{3}{8}$ f) $\frac{3}{5} - \frac{2}{7}$ g) $\frac{2}{7} + \frac{1}{2}$ h) $\frac{9}{10} - \frac{5}{8}$

2 a) $2\frac{1}{7} + 1\frac{3}{4}$ b) $4\frac{4}{5} - 2\frac{2}{3}$ c) $1\frac{5}{6} + 2\frac{2}{3}$ d) $4\frac{1}{4} - 2\frac{3}{5}$

    e) $1\frac{1}{4} + 2\frac{1}{3}$ f) $3\frac{5}{6} - 2\frac{2}{5}$ g) $4\frac{2}{3} - 2\frac{1}{4}$ h) $1\frac{4}{9} + 2\frac{3}{5}$

3 a) $\frac{2}{5} \times \frac{5}{16}$ b) $\frac{1}{3} \div \frac{1}{2}$ c) $\frac{2}{3}$ of $\frac{1}{5}$ d) $\frac{2}{9} \div \frac{1}{3}$

    e) $\frac{3}{8} \div \frac{1}{6}$ f) $\frac{3}{8}$ of 24   g) $\frac{5}{12} \times \frac{10}{15}$ h) $\frac{2}{7} \div \frac{10}{14}$

4 a) $2\frac{1}{6} \times 2\frac{2}{3}$ b) $\frac{5}{6}$ of $3\frac{1}{10}$ c) $3\frac{1}{8} \div 3\frac{3}{4}$ d) $1\frac{3}{5} \times 6\frac{1}{4}$

    e) $\frac{1}{3}$ of $3\frac{3}{4}$ f) $2\frac{11}{12} \div 1\frac{7}{8}$ g) $4\frac{2}{5} \times 1\frac{9}{11}$ h) $3\frac{3}{7} \div 1\frac{13}{28}$

5 a) 40 minutes as a fraction of 2 hours
    b) 30 cm as a fraction of 6 metres
    c) 6 days as a fraction of 2 weeks
    d) 15 hours as a fraction of 4 days

EXERCISE 12.2

Use pencil and paper to work out the answer to each of the following, giving your answer as a fraction in its simplest form.
Then use your calculator to check your answer.

1 $\frac{4}{5} \times \frac{15}{16}$ **2** $\frac{5}{12} - \frac{3}{8}$ **3** $\frac{3}{5} + \frac{5}{8}$ **4** $1\frac{7}{9} \div 1\frac{1}{3}$

5 $\frac{13}{15} - \frac{5}{6}$ **6** $\frac{2}{3}$ of $1\frac{1}{2}$ **7** $\frac{1}{3} + \frac{2}{5}$ **8** $2\frac{2}{3} \div 2\frac{2}{5}$

9 $3\frac{2}{3} - 1\frac{10}{11}$ **10** $\frac{3}{4} \times \frac{5}{9} \times \frac{4}{5}$ **11** $\frac{5}{6} \times \frac{9}{10}$ **12** $3\frac{3}{4} \div 2\frac{1}{2}$

13 $\frac{3}{4}$ of 28   **14** $2\frac{2}{5} + 1\frac{7}{8}$ **15** $\frac{3}{7} - \frac{2}{5}$ **16** $1\frac{2}{3} \div \frac{5}{6}$

17 $1\frac{9}{20} - 1\frac{1}{15}$ **18** $2\frac{1}{4} \times 2\frac{2}{3}$ **19** $4\frac{1}{6} \div 3\frac{3}{4}$ **20** $4\frac{5}{9} + 3\frac{7}{12}$

EXERCISE 12.3

X Express each of these ratios in its simplest form.

1 $6:9$ **2** $18:12$ **3** $25:10$ **4** $48:40$ **5** $20:35:40$

6 $60:100:140$ **7** $14:49:63$ **8** $55:88:220$ **9** $45:60:75$ **10** $18:45:81$

11 Share £150 in the ratio $3:5:7$.

12 Share 120 in the ratio $7:9:14$.

13 Share 60 cm in the ratio $2:3:7$.

14 Share $70 in the ratio $2:5:7$.

15 Share 90 kg in the ratio $1:6:8$.

16 Share £520 in the ratio $3:4:6$.

17 Pete and Lian share some nuts.
Pete takes 5 nuts for every 3 nuts that Lian takes.
There are 48 nuts.
How many **more** nuts does Pete take than Lian?

18 Jean has three daughters.
Michelle is 20 years old, Deborah is
22 years old and Lisa is 24 years old.
Write the ratio of their ages. Give
your answer in its simplest form.

19 Each month Marc spends his money on food,
rent and other expenses in the ratio $2:7:8$.
In January he spent £350 on rent.
a) Work out how much he spent on food in January.
b) Work out how much he spent in total in January.

20 Which of these is the best buy?

15 exercise books
price £3.00

24 exercise books
price £5.40

21 Here are the ingredients for making a
vegetable soup for 12 people:

   6 carrots
   4 onions
   2400 ml stock
   150 g lentils
   12 g thyme

Work out how much of each ingredient is needed to make vegetable soup for 18 people.

EXERCISE 12.4

1 Increase 360 by 18%.

2 Decrease 72 400 by 15%.

3 Increase 1500 by 20%, then by a further 87% of its new value.

4 Jon buys a DVD recorder.
How much VAT does he pay?

Special Offer!
DVD recorder
only £290
plus 17.5% VAT

5 In his first Mathematics test Leo scored 60 marks. In the second test he scored 70 marks. Calculate the percentage increase in his test marks.

6 Lucy bought a new car. She paid £22 000. Each year the value of the car depreciated by 12% of its value at the beginning of that year. Work out the value of Lucy's car:
    a) after one year   **b)** after four years.

7 44% of the students in a school are under 14 years of age.
If there are 650 students in the school, work out how many students in the school are 14 years old or more.

8 Sarah's pocket money this year is £40 per month. Next year she is getting a 22% rise, but 15% of her new pocket money has to be put into a savings account.
    a) Work out Sarah's monthly pocket money for next year.
    b) Work out how much she has to put into a savings account each month next year.

9 Pete bought some items on the internet and then sold them at a garage sale.
What percentage profit or loss has he made on each of these items?
    a) Boots bought for £60, sold for £45   **b)** A CD collection bought for £80, sold for £90

10 John bought a necklace for £120. He sells the necklace to Mia at a profit of 35%.
Mia then sells the necklace to Lily at 45% more than what she paid John for the necklace.
Calculate how much Lily paid for the necklace.

EXERCISE 12.5

This exercise contains a mixture of forwards and reverse percentage problems – so you can train yourself to spot the difference! You should use multiplying factor methods as much as possible.

1 A book shop reduces the prices of all its books by 15% in a sale.
    a) Find the sale price of a book originally priced at £28.
    b) Find the original price of a book that is £17 in the sale.

2 Mr Jones is left with a monthly income of £2028 after 35% deductions have been made.
Work out Mr Jones's monthly salary before any deductions.

3 A pair of sunglasses costs £105.60 inclusive of VAT at 17.5%.
Jerry is told that he does not have to pay the VAT.
Work out how much Jerry should pay.

4 A diet organisation says that you will lose at least 16% of your body weight in 3 months on their special Lighterdiet.
    a) Pat weighs 90 kg. What is the least she should expect to lose if she goes on the Lighterdiet for 3 months?
    b) Tilly weighs 67.2 kg after losing 16% of her body weight on the Lighterdiet. Work out how much she weighed at the start of her diet.

5 A football stadium increases its seating capacity by 20%. It can now seat 1800 people.
Work out its seating capacity before the increase.

6 Sanjay bought a house. He sold it 4 years later for £85 000 after making a profit of 25%.
Work out how much Sanjay paid for the house.

7 The number of students in a school increases by 10%.
As a result the number of teachers the school employs increases by $12\frac{1}{2}$%.
The school had 120 teachers before the increase and has 1210 students after the increase.
a) Work out how many teachers will be employed after the increase.
b) Work out how many students were in the school before the increase.

8 A playground has a rectangular sandpit. The council has the sandpit made into a larger
rectangle. The width of the rectangle is to be increased by 15% to 2.76 m. The length of the
sandpit was 4 m but is to be increased by 25%.
a) Work out the dimensions of the sandpit before it was made larger.
b) Work out the area of the sandpit after it was made larger.

9 A year ago I bought a new car. It depreciates at 24% per year.
My car is presently worth £3800.
a) Work out the value of my car when I bought it.
b) Work out how much my car will be worth three years from now.
Give your answer to the nearest pound (£).

10 The sides of a triangle are increased by 40%.
a) Work out the value of h.
b) Work out the value of b.
c) By what percentage has the area of the triangle
been increased?

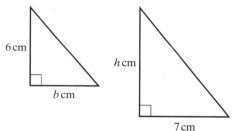

EXERCISE 12.6

1 Work out the simple interest on £2400 invested at 4% per annum for 6 years.

2 Work out the compound interest on £360 invested at 5% per annum for 7 years.

3 Work out the simple interest on £80 invested at 12.5% per annum for 5 years.

4 Work out the compound interest on £8000 invested at 6% per annum for 3 years.

5 £500 is invested at x% compound interest.
After 5 years it has grown to £701 to the nearest pound.
Use a trial and improvement method to find the value of x.

6 William invests some money at a compound interest rate of 10% per annum.
After 4 years his investment is worth £585.64.
How much did William invest?

7 Prakesh receives £2100 for his 21st birthday. His father says he will look after the money and
add 3.5% compound interest to the amount each year.
How old will Prakesh be when this amount of money has increased to £2862?

8 A ten-year savings bond pays 2% interest for the first year, then 4.5% per annum compound interest after that.
Work out the total final value after ten years of an initial investment of £1000.

9 Wendy is investing £300 in a long-term savings scheme.
She can choose between two savings plans.
Savings Plan A: **Simple** interest at 6% per annum.
Savings Plan B: **Compound** interest at 5% per annum.
a) Which plan gives the better return over 3 years?
b) Which plan gives the better return over 10 years?
Justify your answers with numerical calculations.

10 Jasmine invests £100 in a savings account at 3% compound interest.
How many years will it take for Jasmine's investment to exceed £180?

 EXERCISE 12.7

1 Maria invests £300 at 4% compound interest.
Work out how much her investment is worth:
a) after 1 year   **b)** after 2 years   **c)** after 12 years.

2 Penny buys a new car for £20 000. At the end of each year, the value of the car has fallen to 70% of its value at the beginning of that year.
Work out how much Penny's car is worth:
a) after 1 year   **b)** after 2 years   **c)** after 8 years.

3 Ariel invests £470 at 5% compound interest.
Work out how many years it takes until his investment has reached £800.

4 Tamsin pays £2400 for a set of new computers. At the end of each year, the value of the computers has fallen to 65% of their value at the beginning of that year. Tamsin decides to replace her computers once their value has fallen below £500.
Work out how many years it takes until Tamsin replaces her computers.

5 Kevin decides to put £320 into a savings scheme. The scheme pays 6% compound interest for the first year, then 8% compound interest per annum (each year) after that. Work out how much Kevin's savings are worth:
a) after 1 year   **b)** after 2 years   **c)** after 20 years.

6 Here are some instructions for making a number sequence:
• the first term is 4
• to make each new term, multiply the previous one by 2 and add 7.
a) Work out the first three terms of the number sequence.
b) Use your calculator's [ANS] key to help find the value of the 20th term.

U3 CHAPTER 13

Algebraic equations

EXERCISE 13.1A

Look at the various algebraic statements labelled A to J.

A $7x + 2 = 3$ **B** $6y + 5$ **C** πr^2 **D** $V = L \times B \times H$
E $5x - 2x = 3x$ **F** $x^3 = 27$ **G** $2c + 3 = c + 3 + c$ **H** $A = \frac{1}{2}(a + b)h$
I $x^2 - 9$ **J** $12x = 30$

1 Which ones are expressions?   2 Which ones are equations?

3 Which ones would you call formulae?   4 Pick out any identities, and rewrite them using the identity sign, $\equiv$.

EXERCISE 13.1B

1 If $e = 2, f = 4$ and $g = -3$, find the value of:
   a) $(e + f)^2$ **b)** $2f - g$ **c)** $3g + 2ef$ **d)** $(3e - g)^2$

2 If $x = -6, y = -1$ and $z = 9$, find the value of:
   a) $y^2 + 2z$ **b)** $z(x - 10y)$ **c)** $7(2x + 3z)$ **d)** $\dfrac{x + 2z}{2y}$

3 The distance, s, travelled by a particle is given by the formula $s = ut + \frac{1}{2}at^2$ where u is the initial velocity, t is the time and a is the acceleration.
   a) Use your calculator to work out the value of s when $a = 8.5, t = 6.5$ and $u = 1.7$. Write your answer correct to 3 significant figures.
   b) Use your calculator to work out the value of u when $s = 29.3, t = 4$ and $a = -2$. Write your answer correct to 3 significant figures.

4 The time T travelled is given by the formula $T = \dfrac{D}{S}$.
   a) Find the exact value of T when $D = 322$ and $S = 23$.
   b) Find the value of D when $T = 5.2$ and $S = 63.5$.

EXERCISE 13.2

Solve these algebraic equations. Use a formal method, and show the steps of your working.

1 $8t = 48$ **2** $u - 6 = 4$ **3** $\frac{1}{4}p = 5$ **4** $20g = 10$ **5** $5q = 1$

6 $w + 8 = 3$ **7** $6y = 5$ **8** $y + 12 = 5$ **9** $\dfrac{p}{6} = -3$ **10** $\dfrac{c}{7} = \dfrac{3}{4}$

Find the values of the letters in each of these equations.

11 $a - 3 = 6$ **12** $7b = 77$ **13** $5c = 17$ **14** $15 = 28 - d$

15 $12 - e = 12$ **16** $8f = 2$ **17** $20 = 30 - g$ **18** $h^2 = 36$

19 $4i^2 = 4$ **20** $w + 8 = 23$

EXERCISE 13.3

 Solve these algebraic equations, showing the steps of your working clearly.
All the answers should be integers, but some may be negative.

1 $3x + 2 = x + 12$ **2** $22 + 5x = 6x$ **3** $9x + 4 = 4x + 29$

4 $x + 5 = 13 - x$ **5** $8x + 3 = 48 - x$ **6** $23 - 2x = 33 - 7x$

7 $5x + 3 = 15 - x$ **8** $7 + 4x = 2x + 9$ **9** $8x - 5 = x + 9$

10 $6x = 42 - x$

Solve these algebraic equations, showing the steps of your working clearly.
Answers should be given as top-heavy fractions or mixed numbers, rather than decimals.

11 $6a + 5 = 3a + 6$ **12** $2b + 7 = 9b - 3$ **13** $8c - 5 = 3c - 2$

14 $9d + 1 = 17 - 3d$ **15** $5e + 12 = e + 3$ **16** $10f - 3 = 11f - 1$

17 $4g - 9 = 2 + g$ **18** $7h - 2 = 6 + 4h$ **19** $i + 4 = 7 - i$

20 $3j - 4 = 5 + 10j$

EXERCISE 13.4

Multiply out the brackets, and hence solve these equations. Show each step of your working.

1 $6(x - 3) + 2 = 14$ **2** $3(x - 4) = 23 - 2x$

3 $4(x + 10) = 50 - x$ **4** $8(x - 3) = 8$

5 $2(5x + 3) = 7x + 24$ **6** $x + 7 = 5(x - 1)$

7 $4(3x - 5) = 3(2x + 1) + 1$ **8** $5(x - 1) = 3(x - 5)$

9 $7(x + 8) = 4(x + 7) - 11$ **10** $2(5x + 3) = 4(x - 3)$

11 $6(x + 3) - 4(2x - 3) = 10$ **12** $3x - 7 = 6x - 5(2x + 1)$

Write an equation, involving brackets, to formulate each of the next three problems.
Then expand your brackets and solve the equation, to obtain the answer to the problem.

13 Ben earned y euros per hour in January.
In February his earnings were increased by 2 euros per hour.
a) Write down an expression, in terms of y, for Ben's new earnings per hour.
b) Write down an expression, using brackets, for Ben's earnings if he works for 10 hours in
February.

14 Simon thinks of a number. He multiplies it by 7 and then adds 5 to the new total.
  a) Write down an expression for this information. Use n for Simon's mystery number.
  Simon gets the same answer when he adds 29 to his mystery number.
  b) Write down an equation for this information.
  c) Solve your equation to find Simon's mystery number.

15 Michael and Tanya each think of the same number.
  Michael multiplies the number by 4, and then adds 2.
  Tanya adds 4 to the number, and then multiplies the answer by 2.
  They both end up with the same answer.
  a) Write this information as an equation.
  b) Solve your equation to find the number they both thought of.

EXERCISE 13.5

Solve these equations.

1 $\dfrac{x+2}{2} = \dfrac{x+1}{3}$

2 $\dfrac{x+2}{5} = 5$

3 $\dfrac{4x+3}{5} = \dfrac{x+3}{2}$

4 $\dfrac{5x}{8} - \dfrac{x}{4} = 1$

5 $\dfrac{x+4}{5} = \dfrac{x}{3}$

6 $\dfrac{7x-4}{3} = x - 3$

7 $\dfrac{x-5}{2} = \dfrac{x-3}{4}$

8 $\dfrac{3x+7}{4} = \dfrac{2x+11}{9}$

9 $\dfrac{x+2}{10} = \dfrac{4-x}{5}$

10 $\dfrac{2x+7}{6} + \dfrac{5x-5}{3} = 0$

EXERCISE 13.6

1

a) Form an equation in x.
b) Hence work out the size of the largest angle.

2

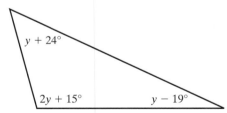

a) Form and solve an equation in y.
b) Hence find the sizes of the angles in the triangle.

3 A triangle has angles $x + 20°$, $3x - 10°$ and $70°$.
  a) Set up an equation in x.
  b) Solve your equation to find the value of x.
  c) Work out the sizes of the angles in the triangle.

4 The angles in a triangle are $y + 10°$, $7y - 30°$ and $3y - 20°$.
  a) Set up an equation in y.
  b) Solve your equation to find the value of y.
  c) Work out the sizes of the angles in the triangle.

5 The diagram shows a quadrilateral.
Work out the size of the angle marked *f*.

6 The diagram shows a quadrilateral.

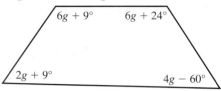

a) Form and solve an equation in *g*.
b) Hence find the sizes of the angles in the quadrilateral.
c) What is the special name for this type of quadrilateral?

7 The diagram shows a quadrilateral.

a) Form an equation in *y*.
b) Solve your equation to find *y*.
c) Hence find the size of each angle in the quadrilateral.

8 The diagram shows some angles.

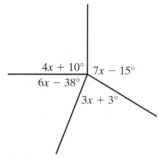

a) Set up an equation in *x*.
b) Solve your equation to find the value of *x*.
c) Work out the size of each angle.
d) Check that your four angles add up to 360°.

EXERCISE 13.7

1 A square has sides of length *m* cm. Obtain a formula for the perimeter, *P*, of the square.

2 A square has length *g* cm.
Write down a formula in terms of *g* for:
a) the perimeter, *P*, of the square
b) the area, *A*, of the square.

g cm

3 A rectangle has width *x* cm.
Its length is 10 cm more than its width.
Write down a formula in terms of *x* for:
a) the length, *L*, of the rectangle
b) the perimeter, *P*, of the rectangle
c) the area, *A*, of the rectangle.

x cm

4 Becky buys *n* books at £*p* each.
Write an equation for the total cost, *C*, of the books that Becky buys.

5 Pens cost 5p each and pencils cost 8p each.
Nick buys x pens and y pencils.
   a) Write down an expression in terms of x and y for the total number of pens and pencils he buys.
   b) If the total cost is z pounds, write down an equation for the total cost in terms of x, y and z.

6 The cost of renting a machine is £20 plus a daily charge of £5 per day.
   a) Find the cost of hiring the machine for 6 days.
   b) Obtain a formula for the cost, £C, of hiring the machine for x days.

7 In a school there are g girls and b boys.
   a) Write an expression for the total number of students in the school.
   b) Write a formula for the total number of students, N, in the school.

8 On Monday, Melissa runs p kilometres per hour for q hours.
Write down a formula for the total distance, D, that Melissa runs on Monday.

9 The diagram shows a large rectangle divided into four smaller shapes labelled P, Q, R and S.
P is a square with each side c cm and S is a rectangle with base 9 cm and height h cm.
   a) Find an expression for the area of rectangle Q.
   b) Find a formula for the area, A cm^2, of the large rectangle.

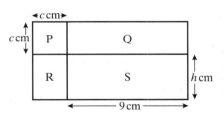

10 A rectangle of dimensions 8 cm by 5 cm has a square of sides x cm cut out from each of its four corners. The sides thus formed are then folded up to make a rectangular tray.
   a) Find an expression for the area of the base of the tray.
   b) Find a formula for the volume, V cm^3, of the rectangular tray.

EXERCISE 13.8

Rearrange these formulae so that the indicated letter becomes the subject.

1 $A = lw$ (w) **2** $P = 2b + 2h$ (h) **3** $y = 5x - 2$ (x)

4 $D = s \times t$ (t) **5** $E = \dfrac{360}{n}$ (n) **6** $S = 180(n - 2)$ (n)

7 $C = \pi d$ (d) **8** $T = x(y - z)$ (x) **9** $v = u + at$ (t)

10 $m = \dfrac{y}{x}$ (y) **11** $x^2 = 2bh$ (b) **12** $v = u + ft$ (t)

13 $a = \sqrt{x + 3}$ (x) **14** $a^2 = c^2 - b^2$ (c) **15** $y = x^2 + 5$ (x)

16 $y = \dfrac{3}{x}$ (x) **17** $v^2 = u^2 + 2as$ (a) **18** $V = \pi r^2 h$ (r)

19 $A = \frac{1}{2}(a + b)h$ (a) **20** $F = 32 + \dfrac{9C}{5}$ (C)

EXERCISE 13.9

Use trial and improvement to solve these equations correct to 1 decimal place.

1 The equation $x^2 + 3x = 24$ has a solution between $x = 3$ and $x = 4$.

2 The equation $x^2 + x = 33$ has a solution between $x = 5$ and $x = 6$.

3 The equation $x^3 + x = 4$ has a solution between $x = 1$ and $x = 2$.

4 The equation $x^2 - 5x = 20$ has a solution between $x = 7$ and $x = 8$.

5 The equation $x^3 + 5x = 117$ has a solution between $x = 4$ and $x = 5$.

6 The equation $x^2 - 3x = 50.5$ has a solution between $x = 8$ and $x = 9$.

7 The equation $2x^2 + x = 2$ has a solution between $x = 0$ and $x = 1$.

Use trial and improvement to solve these equations correct to 2 decimal places.

8 The equation $2x^3 - x = 500$ has a solution between $x = 6$ and $x = 7$.

9 The equation $x^2(x + 1) = 34$ has a solution between 2 and 3.

10 The equation $x^2 + 2x = 7$ has a solution between $x = 1$ and $x = 2$.

EXERCISE 13.10

Simplify these expressions using the index laws $x^a \times x^b = x^{a+b}$ and $x^a \div x^b = x^{a-b}$.

1 $x^4 \times x^3$ **2** $y^{15} \div y^5$ **3** $z \times z^8 \times z^2$ **4** $4x^2 \times 6x^5$

5 $8x^9 \times 3x$ **6** $40y^6 \div 5y^3$ **7** $2y^5 \times 5y^2$ **8** $27z^{27} \div 9z^9$

9 $3x^4 \times 2x \times 7x^3$ **10** $6z^9 \div 12z$

Simplify these expressions using the index law $(x^a)^n = x^{a \times n}$.

11 $(x^4)^2$ **12** $(y^8)^3$ **13** $(3z^5)^3$ **14** $(9x^6)^2$ **15** $(y^{12})^5$

16 $(5z^5)^3$ **17** $(7x^4)^2$ **18** $(2x^9)^3$ **19** $(10x^5y^3)^4$ **20** $(4x^{10}y)^2$

Simplify these expressions.

21 $7x^5 \times 5x^3$ **22** $60y^7 \div 15y^2$ **23** $(8z^5)^2$ **24** $35y^2 \div 5y$

25 $(6x^8)^2$ **26** $32x^9 \div 8x^7$ **27** $3x \times 12x^4 \times 2x^2$ **28** $(4x^2y^7)^2$

29 $(x^{12}y^{11})^4$ **30** $3x \times 15x^4$

U3 CHAPTER 14

Graphs of straight lines

EXERCISE 14.1

Find the gradient (m) and the y-intercept (c) for each of the drawn lines, or lines joining the given coordinates in questions **1** to **8**.

1

2

3

4

(2,3)

(6,1)

5

6

(7,6)

(0,3)

7

8

(5,5)

(3,1)

EXERCISE 14.2 pt

1 to 8 Write down the equations of the straight lines whose gradients and y-intercepts you found in Exercise 14.1, questions **1** to **8**.

9 The diagram shows the graph of a linear function in x.
   a) Find the gradient and y-intercept of the line.
   b) Hence write down the equation of the straight line.

10 The diagram shows the graph corresponding to a linear function of x.

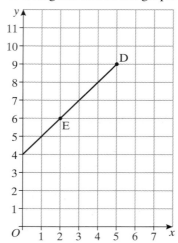

a)   Write down the coordinates of the points D and E on the line.
b)   Find the gradient and y-intercept of the line.
c)   Hence write down the equation of the straight line.

EXERCISE 14.3

1 Rearrange each of these equations into the form $y = ax + b$.
Pick out the two that represent a pair of parallel lines.
a) $x + y = 5$ b) $2x + y = 5$
c) $y - 8 - x = 0$ d) $x - y + 5 = 0$

2 Look at this list of equations.
There are four pairs of parallel lines, and one odd one out.

$y = 3x - 2$	$y = 7x + 3$	$y = 2 + 7x$
$y = 2x + 3$	$3 - y = 2x$	$y + 5x = 7$
$y + 2x = 7$	$y - 3x + 4 = 0$	$2y = 3 - 10x$

a)   Pick out the four pairs of parallel lines.
b)   Suggest the equation of another line that is parallel to the odd one out.

3 The line $y = ax + b$ is parallel to $y = 6x - 2$, and passes through the point $(0, -5)$.
a)   Write down the value of a.
b)   Work out the value of b, and hence obtain the equation of the line.

4 The line $y = mx + c$ is parallel to the line $y = 4 - x$, and passes through the point $(2, 0)$.
a)   Find the values of m and c, and write down the equation of the line.
b)   The line also passes through the point $(7, p)$. Find p.

5 A line has equation $\dfrac{y + 3}{4} = x$.

a)   Rearrange the equation into the form $y = mx + c$.
b)   Find the equation of the parallel line that passes through the point $(1, 9)$.

U3 CHAPTER 15

Simultaneous equations

EXERCISE 15.1

Solve these problems using the method of inspection. Write out all the stages clearly.

1 $2x + y = 7$
   $x + y = 4$

2 $5x + 2y = 20$
   $4x + 2y = 18$

3 $x + 4y = 11$
   $x + y = 5$

4 $x + 5y = 9$
   $x + 2y = 3$

5 $5x - 2y = 14$
   $3x - 2y = 6$

6 $x + 4y = 21$
   $x + 2y = 13$

7 $3x + 4y = 42$
   $x + 4y = 30$

8 $5x + y = 13$
   $5x + 4y = 22$

9 $2x - 3y = 8$
   $x - 3y = 1$

10 $2x + y = 9$
    $2x + 5y = 13$

EXERCISE 15.2

Solve questions **1** to **8** using the algebraic *addition* method, showing all your working clearly.

1 $4x + y = 9$
   $2x - y = 3$

2 $x + y = 8$
   $-x + 2y = 13$

3 $3x - y = 1$
   $x + y = 3$

4 $3x + y = 9$
   $2x - y = 1$

5 $x + y = 7$
   $2x - y = 2$

6 $-x + 2y = 7$
   $x + 5y = 14$

7 $3x + y = 10$
   $2x - y = 10$

8 $x - 2y = 6$
   $3x + 2y = 6$

Solve questions **9** to **16** using the algebraic *subtraction* method, showing all your working clearly.

9 $2x + y = 12$
   $x + y = 7$

10 $2x + y = 7$
    $2x + 3y = 9$

11 $2x + 3y = 8$
    $2x + y = -4$

12 $8x + 3y = 23$
    $2x + 3y = 17$

13 $5x + y = 14$
    $2x + y = 8$

14 $7x + 3y = 23$
    $7x + 6y = 32$

15 $3x + 5y = 31$
    $x + 5y = 17$

16 $5x + 3y = 26$
    $2x + 3y = 14$

Solve questions **17** to **32** using algebra.
For each question you will have to decide whether to add or subtract.

17 $3x + 2y = 8$
    $2x - y = 3$

18 $4x + 3y = -1$
    $-3x + 2y = 5$

19 $x + 4y = 6$
    $3x - 2y = 4$

20 $3x + 5y = 21$
    $4x - 2y = 2$

21 $3x + 4y = 23$
    $2x + 5y = 20$

22 $4x + 2y = 22$
    $x - y = 4$

23 $3x - 2y = -10$
    $x + 6y = 0$

24 $2x - 3y = -17$
    $3x + y = -9$

25	$5x + 2y = 1$ $8x + 3y = 2$	26	$2x + 5y = 16$ $x - y = -6$	27	$5x - 4y = 24$ $2x - y = 9$	28	$4x - 5y = 17$ $3x - 4y = 13$
29	$2x + 3y = 1$ $3x + 2y = 9$	30	$5x + 2y = 11$ $3x - 4y = 4$	31	$8x - 3y = 6$ $2x - y = 1$	32	$3x + 5y = -21$ $x - 4y = 10$

EXERCISE 15.3

For each of these questions draw a set of coordinate axes on squared paper (or graph paper). Draw the lines corresponding to each equation, and hence solve the simultaneous equations graphically.

1	$x + y = 3$ $x + 2y = 5$	2	$y = 2x + 7$ $x + y = 1$	3	$2x + y = 2$ $y = x + 5$	4	$y = 2x - 1$ $y - x = 2$
5	$3x + 2y = 6$ $5x - 2y = 10$	6	$y = x + 3$ $x + y = 1$	7	$y = 2x + 1$ $x - 2y = 4$	8	$x + y = 2$ $y = -\frac{1}{2}x$

EXERCISE 15.4

Use simultaneous equations to help you solve the following problems. Remember to show all your working carefully.

1   In a sale, Pete buys 4 pairs of trousers and 3 shirts for £94 and Andy buys 5 pairs of trousers and 6 shirts for £135.50.
   a)   Write two simultaneous equations to express this information.
   b)   Solve your equations to find the price of a pair of trousers and the price of a shirt.

2   A hire company has a fleet of coaches and minibuses.
   2 coaches and 6 minibuses can carry 204 passengers.
   3 coaches and 5 minibuses can carry 242 passengers.
   a)   Write two simultaneous equations to express this information.
   b)   How many passengers can one coach carry?

3   Nick and Diana go to a shop to buy some wool to make a jumper.
   Nick buys 3 balls of red wool and 4 balls of white wool for £11.30.
   Diana buys 5 balls of red wool and 3 balls of white wool for £12.60.
   a)   Write two simultaneous equations to express this information.
   b)   Solve your equations to find the cost of a ball of wool in each colour.

4   At a stall, May buys 3 packets of crisps and 5 cans of cola for £4.30, whilst Jerry buys 5 packets of crisps and 4 cans of cola for £5.
   a)   Write two simultaneous equations to express this information.
        Explain the meaning of the symbols you use.
   b)   Solve your equations to find the cost of a packet of crisps and the cost of a can of cola.

5   On Tuesday some teachers took some students to the local theatre.
   Miss Tobias paid £62 for 3 teachers and 20 students.
   Mr Angus paid £95 for 5 teachers and 30 students.
   Work out the cost of an adult ticket and the cost of a student ticket.

U3 CHAPTER 16

Inequalities

EXERCISE 16.1

Find the whole number (integer) solutions to each of these inequalities.

1 $x > 5$

2 $2x > 7$

3 $y < 3$

4 $4y < 10$

5 $2 < y \leqslant 7$

6 $6 \leqslant 3g \leqslant 16$

7 $5 < x < 9$

8 $8 \leqslant 2m \leqslant 23$

9 $3 < f - 2 < 9$

10 $4 < 3d < 12$

11 $7 \leqslant y \leqslant 10$

12 $9 \leqslant 2x \leqslant 15$

13 $5x \leqslant 30$

14 $4p > 13$

15 $3 < 2x - 1 \leqslant 17$

16 $1 \leqslant w \leqslant 7$

17 $5 \leqslant g - 3 \leqslant 12$

18 $8 < 5c \leqslant 20$

19 $17 \leqslant p + 2 \leqslant 18$

20 $-4 < v < 1$

EXERCISE 16.2

Solve, algebraically, the inequalities in questions **1** to **20**.

1 $x + 8 \geqslant 20$

2 $2x + 1 > 15$

3 $8x - 27 < 13$

4 $3 - x < 15 + x$

5 $4x - 1 < x + 8$

6 $5x + 12 \leqslant 18 + x$

7 $8x \geqslant x - 35$

8 $53 + x < 17 + 3x$

9 $21 - x \leqslant 11 + 4x$

10 $4(x + 1) > x + 10$

11 $x + 19 \geqslant 29 - 5x$

12 $7x - 2 < 30$

13 $34 + x > 6 - 5x$

14 $x - 12 \leqslant 11 - x$

15 $8x + 3 \leqslant x + 3$

16 $10 - x < 3x + 5$

17 $500 \geqslant 230 - 9x$

18 $8 + 5x < 8 - x$

19 $3(x - 5) \geqslant x - 8$

20 $7(3x + 2) < 5(x - 1)$

21 Solve the inequality $\dfrac{x}{8} - 2 \leqslant 1$

22 Solve the inequality $\dfrac{2x + 3}{5} > 4$

23 Solve the inequality $\dfrac{4x - 1}{2} > 7$

24 Solve the inequality $\dfrac{7x + 8}{3} > 2$

EXERCISE 16.3

In questions **1** to **10** you are given the solution to an inequality.
Draw a suitable number line diagram to illustrate the solution in each case.

1 $x < -4$

2 $x \geqslant -3$

3 $2 \leqslant x \leqslant 7$

4 $-4 < x < -1$

5 $x \leqslant 2$

6 $x < 10$

7 $-4 < x < 0$

8 $-9 < x \leqslant -4$

9 $-1 \leqslant x \leqslant 4$

10 $x > 3.5$

In questions **11** to **20**, solve each inequality and then illustrate it with a number line diagram.

11 $4 + x < 17$ **12** $5x - 1 \leqslant 24$ **13** $18 - x > 8$ **14** $6x + 11 \geqslant 41$

15 $7 < 2x < 24$ **16** $3 - x < 4x - 7$ **17** $5x - 2 \leqslant x + 3$ **18** $7x + 2 < 18 - x$

19 $5 + 2x < x - 1$ **20** $x - 3 \leqslant 3(x + 4)$

EXERCISE 16.4 pt

For each of questions **1** to **5**, draw a coordinate grid on which x and y can range from -5 to 5.

1 Draw the graphs of these straight lines: $x = 1, x = 4, y = 3$ and $y = x$.
Hence shade the region R corresponding to the inequalities: $x \geqslant 1, x < 4, y < 3, y \leqslant x$.

2 Draw the graphs of these straight lines: $x = 4, y = 1, y = 5$ and $y = x - 1$.
Hence shade the region R corresponding to the inequalities: $x < 4, y > 1, y < 5, y > x - 1$.

3 Draw the graphs of these straight lines: $x = -3, y = 2$ and $y = x$.
Hence shade the region R corresponding to the inequalities: $x > -3, y < 2, y > x$.

4 Shade the region R corresponding to the inequalities: $x \geqslant -1, x \leqslant 3, y \geqslant -1, x + y \leqslant 4$.

5 Shade the region R corresponding to the inequalities: $x < 1, y < 0, y < x + 1, x + y > -3$.

6 The diagram shows a region T bounded by three straight lines, P, Q and R.
a) Write down the equations of the three straight lines, P, Q and R.
Show clearly which equation applies to which line.
b) Write down three inequalities that define the region **T**.

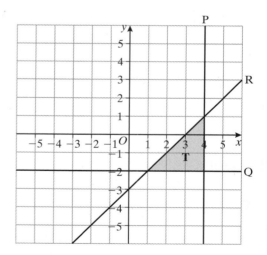

U3 CHAPTER 17

Travel and other graphs

EXERCISE 17.1

1 Uzma cycles to her friend's house.
Here is a description of her journey:

- Uzma leaves her house at 8 am.
- She cycles 10 km to arrive at her friend's house at 9.30 am.
- Uzma spends 75 minutes with her friend.
- Uzma then cycles back towards her home but stops after 4 km, at 11.15 am to have a rest.
- She rests for $\frac{1}{4}$ hour.
- She then cycles straight home, arriving at 12.30 pm.

a) Draw a travel graph of Uzma's journey.

b) What is Uzma's average speed, in km per hour, on her way to her friend's house?

2 The diagram shows a vase.
It is in the shape of a
cuboid. Water is poured
into the vase at a steady
rate.

  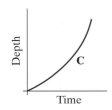

Say which of graphs A, B or C best describes how the depth of water in the vase varies over time. Explain your reasoning.

3 Zac climbs a steep hill.
He gains height at a rate of 5 metres per minute.
It takes him 1 hour to reach the top.
He then stops for 45 minutes to have lunch.
Then he descends, at 10 metres per minute.

a) How high is the hill?

b) How long does Zac's descent take?

c) Copy and complete the graph,
numbering the scales on both axes.

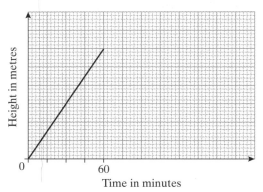

4 Water is poured into a container at a constant rate.
The container is in the shape of a cone, as shown in
the diagram.
Sketch a set of depth/time axes, and complete the
diagram to show how the depth of water in the
container changes over time.

 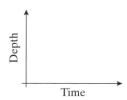

5 Jean saves some money each month.
She saves £20 in the first month and then
saves £30 per month after that.

Number of months (n)	1	2	3	4
Total amount saved (T)	20	50		

    a) Copy and complete the table, to show the
total amount saved over the first four months.

    b) Find a formula for T in terms of n.

    c) Draw a graph to show how much Jean saves in 1 year.

Jean needs to save £250.

    d) Use your graph to find out how long it will take Jean to save £250.

    e) Use your formula to work out how many months it will take Jean to save £980.

6 Water runs out of a hole in the bottom of a
container.
The water runs out at a steady rate.
The graph shows how the depth of water in the
container varies over time.

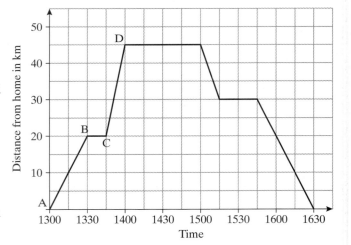

Say which of containers A, B or C best matches
this graph.
Explain your reasoning.

EXERCISE 17.2

1 One Saturday, Maya drives from
Liverpool to Manchester to visit her
grandmother.
She stops along the way to get some
flowers.
On her way home she stops for petrol
and a coffee before returning to
Liverpool.
The travel graph shows her journey.

    a) How long does Maya stop for
flowers?

    b) What time does Maya get to her
grandmother?

    c) How far is her grandmother from
Maya's house?

    d) How long did Maya stop for
petrol and coffee?

    e) Is Maya's speed greater between A and B or between C and D?
Explain how you can tell.

    f) What time does Maya arrive home?

2 The diagram shows a distance–time graph for a train travelling between Farham and Gradel.

The train leaves Farham at 1400 for its outward journey to Gradel.
The train leaves Gradel at 1640 for its return journey to Farham.
a) Work out the speed of the train on its journey from Gradel to Farham.
b) State one difference between the outward journey and the return journey.
c) State one thing that is the same on the outward journey and the return journey.

At 1500 a second train leaves Gradel.
It travels towards Farham at a constant speed of 40 miles per hour.
d) On a copy of the graph, draw the journey of the second train.
e) At what time do the two trains pass each other?

3 Tess owns a car hire company.
The cost of hiring a car is £60 for the first day and then £36 per day after that.
a) Copy and complete this table to show the cost in £(C) to hire a car from Tess's car hire company by the end of each of the first four days.

Day number (n)	Total cost in £ (C)
1	
2	
3	
4	

b) Construct a graph to show the total cost by the end of each of the first 10 days.
c) Add a second line to your graph to show the cost if Tess had charged the same amount of £40 per day from the start.
d) At the end of which day would the cost be the same for both types of charges?
e) Write down two formulae for C, in terms of n, for the cost of hiring a car for n days using the two charging methods.

4 A group of hikers are hiking from their camp to a ruined castle.
They set off from their camp at 0800.
They walk for 2 hours at 3 km per hour.
They stop for a 30 minute rest.
After the rest, they walk on for a further $2\frac{1}{2}$ hours at 4 km per hour.
Then they stop for lunch for 1 hour.
After lunch, they walk on for a further 2 hours at 4 km per hour until they reach the ruined castle.

a) On a copy of this grid, complete the travel graph.
b) How far is the ruined castle from the camp?

EXERCISE 17.3

1 Leo goes out in his car. He accelerates at a constant rate for the first 30 seconds, then travels at a steady velocity for the next 2 minutes. He then sees a pedestrian crossing ahead, so he slows down at a constant rate until he sees the pedestrian has crossed the road, before continuing at a steady velocity again.
The diagram below shows these parts of his journey, with corresponding line segments AB, BC, CD and DE.

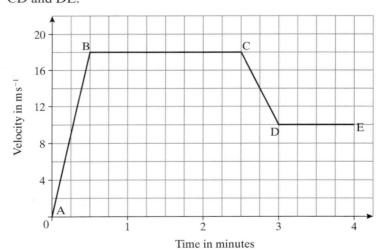

a) Work out Leo's acceleration during the first 30 seconds of his journey.
b) Write down the maximum velocity during his journey.
c) Work out how far Leo travelled during the section of the journey marked BC on the diagram.
d) Did Leo stop at the pedestrian crossing?

2 A spacecraft accelerates from rest to a speed of 3200 m s^{-1} in 3 minutes.
a) Convert 3 minutes into seconds.
b) Work out the acceleration of the spacecraft, in m s^{-2}.

3 A particle accelerates and then maintains a constant velocity before it decelerates and comes to rest again.
The velocity–time graph shows the movement of the particle.

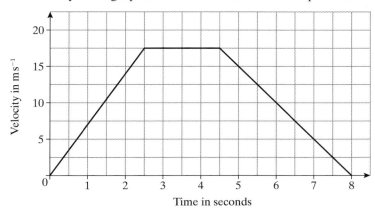

a) Work out the acceleration of the particle during the first $2\frac{1}{2}$ seconds.
b) Work out the distance the particle travels when it maintains a steady velocity.
c) Work out the deceleration of the particle.

4 A motorbike is travelling at a constant velocity of $20\,\text{m s}^{-1}$ from point A.
It continues at this velocity for 12 seconds until it reaches point B.
It then decelerates uniformly over the next 3 seconds to $15\,\text{m s}^{-1}$ to point C.
It continues at this new velocity for 18 seconds, to reach point D.

a) Illustrate this information on a velocity–time graph.
Indicate the points A, B, C and D on your graph.

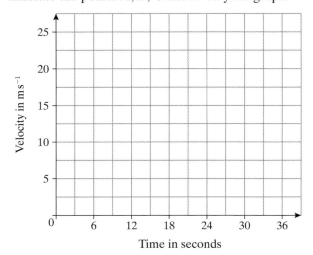

b) Work out how far the motorbike travels between points A and B.
c) Work out how far the motorbike travels between points C and D.

U3 CHAPTER 18

Circles and cylinders

EXERCISE 18.1

1   A circle has radius 11 mm. Find its circumference, correct to 3 significant figures.

2   A circle has diameter 30 cm. Find its circumference, correct to 3 significant figures.

3   A circle has radius 15 cm. Find its area, correct to 3 significant figures.

4   A circle has diameter 42.8 cm. Find its area, correct to 3 significant figures.

5   Find, correct to 4 significant figures, the circumference of a circle with radius 37.18 cm.

6   Find, correct to 3 significant figures, the area of a circle with diameter 53.74 mm.

7   Find, correct to 4 significant figures, the circumference of a circle with diameter 3.06 cm.

8   Find, correct to 4 significant figures, the area of a circle with radius 0.924 cm.

Give the answers to each of these problems correct to 3 significant figures.

9   A circle has diameter 13 cm. Find its area.

10   A circle has radius 0.43 mm. Find its area.

11   A circle has diameter 370 cm. Find its circumference.

12   A circle has radius 8.05 m. Find its circumference.

13   A circle has a diameter of 24 mm. Calculate its circumference.

14   A face of a coin is a circle of diameter of 32.4 mm. Calculate its area.

15   Anna decides to run around a circular race track.
The radius of the track is 30 metres.
a)   Work out the length of one lap of the track.

Anna wants to run at least 2000 metres.
She wants to run a whole number of laps.
b)   Work out the minimum number of laps that Anna must run.

16 The diagram shows a rectangle inside a circle.
The circle has a radius of 50 cm.
The rectangle measures 80 cm by 60 cm.
The corners of the rectangle are on the circumference of the circle.
   a) Work out the area of the rectangle.
   b) Work out the area of the circle.
   c) Work out the shaded area.
      Give your answer correct to the nearest square centimetre.

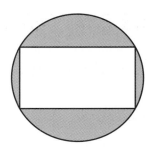

17 The diagram shows a rectangular piece of card
with four circles cut out of it.
The circles are each of diameter 5 cm.
The rectangle measures 24 cm by 13 cm.
   a) Calculate the area of one of the circular holes.
   b) Work out the area of the card.

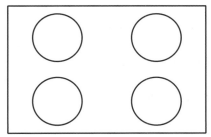

18 A circular table stands on a circular base.
The diameter of the table top is 94 cm.
The radius of the base is 33 cm.
   a) Calculate the area of the table top.
   b) Calculate the circumference of the base.

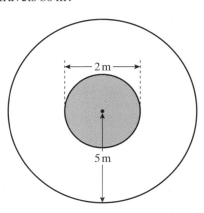

19 A bicycle wheel has a diameter of 70 cm.
   a) How far, in metres, does the wheel go when it completes one revolution?
   b) How far, in metres, does the wheel go when it completes 20 revolutions?
   c) How many revolutions does the wheel complete when it travels 80 m?

20 The diagram shows a circular garden with a circular pond
in the middle.
The whole garden, apart from the pond, is lawn.
The garden has a radius of 5 m.
The pond has a diameter of 2 m.
   a) Calculate the area of the pond.
   b) Calculate the area of the garden.
   c) Hence find the area of the lawn.

The gardener wants to put some fertiliser on the lawn.
1 bag of fertiliser is sufficient for 0.8 m².
   d) Work out how many bags of fertiliser the gardener
      needs to buy.

21 The diagram shows a running track at a school.
It is made up of two straight sections, and two semicircular ends.
The dimensions are marked on the diagram.
Andy runs around the outside boundary of the track, marked with a solid line.
Colin runs around the inside boundary, marked with a dotted line.
They each run one lap of the track.
a) Work out how far Colin runs.
b) Work out how much further Andy runs than Colin.

EXERCISE 18.2

Calculate the perimeter and area of each sector. Give each answer correct to 3 significant figures.

1

8 cm

39°

8 cm

2

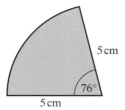

5 cm

76°

5 cm

3

135°

6.7 cm

6.7 cm

4

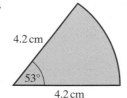

4.2 cm

53°

4.2 cm

5

37 mm

18°

37 mm

6

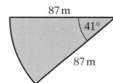

87 m

41°

87 m

7

156°

9.5 cm

9.5 cm

8

3.6 cm

3.6 cm

9 Bob displays some statistical data in a pie chart.
The three sectors of the pie chart are to have angles of 210°, 50° and 100°.
The radius of the pie chart is 7 cm.
a) Work out the area of each sector of Bob's pie chart.
b) Work out the perimeter of the smallest sector.

10 A pizza of diameter 18 inches is to be shared between 10 people. It is cut into ten equal sectors.
a) Work out the angles at the centre of each sector of pizza.
b) Work out the area of one sector.

EXERCISE 18.3

Give the answers to each of these problems correct to 3 significant figures.

1 A circle has circumference 28 mm. Find its radius.

2 A circle has circumference 38.2 cm. Find its diameter.

3 A circle has area 120 cm². Find its radius.

4 A circle has area 60 cm². Find its radius.

5 A circle has circumference 74 m. Find its diameter.

6 A circle has area 850 cm². Find its diameter.

7 A circle has circumference 7.9 cm. Find its diameter.

8 A circle has area 483 cm². Find its radius.

9 The diagram shows a sector of a circle.
The radius of the sector is r centimetres.
The area of the sector is 26.1 cm².
a) Work out the area of the corresponding complete circle.
b) Hence find the value of r.
c) Calculate the perimeter of the sector.

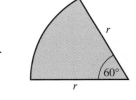

10 The diagram shows a running track.
The ends are semicircles of radius y metres.
The straight sections are of length 45 metres each.
The total distance around the track is 120 metres.
a) Calculate the value of y.
b) Calculate the area contained within the running track.

EXERCISE 18.4

Give the answers to each of these problems correct to 3 significant figures.

1 A cylinder has radius 15 cm and height 23 cm. Find its volume.

2 A cylinder has radius 4 cm and height 3 cm. Find its curved surface area.

3 A cylinder has diameter 36 cm and height 10 cm.
a) Find its volume.
b) Find its curved surface area.

4 A cylinder has radius 7 cm and height 18 cm. Find its volume.

5 The diagram shows a hollow cylinder.
   Work out the curved surface area of the cylinder.

26 cm

34 cm

6 A hollow cylindrical pipeline has an internal diameter of 16 cm.
   The pipeline is 250 metres in length.
   a) Work out the volume of the pipeline.
      Give your answer in cm^3.
   b) $1000 \, cm^3 = 1$ litre
      Express the volume of the pipeline in litres.

7 A tube of crisps is in the shape of a cylinder.
   It has radius 7 cm and height 30 cm.
   Work out the volume of the tube.

8 A sweet packet is in the shape of a hollow cardboard cylinder.
   The inside diameter of the cylinder is 4.5 cm and it has a height of 12 cm.
   a) Work out the volume of the cylinder.

   The sweets have a volume of 2.3 cm^3 each.
   b) Show that the packet cannot contain as many as 90 sweets.

9 Rosie wants to buy a can of soup.
   She wants to buy the can of soup that has the greatest volume.

A

22 cm

12 cm

B

11 cm

25 cm

Which of these two cans should she buy?
Show all your working.

10 A cylinder of radius 6.2 cm has a volume of 1183 cm^3, correct to 4 significant figures.
   Work out the height of the cylinder.

X EXERCISE 18.5

1 A circle has diameter 30 cm. Work out:
a) its circumference **b)** its area.
Leave your answers in terms of π.

2 A circle has radius 18 cm. Work out:
a) its circumference **b)** its area.
Leave your answers in terms of π.

3 A cylinder has radius 10 cm and height 7 cm. Work out:
a) its curved surface area **b)** its volume.
Leave your answers in terms of π.

4 A circle has circumference 39π cm.
a) Work out the exact radius of the circle.
b) Work out the exact area of the circle.
Leave your answers in terms of π.

5 A circle has a circumference of 5π cm.
a) Work out the exact radius of the circle.
b) Work out the exact area of the circle.
Leave your answers in terms of π.

6 A cylinder has volume 580π cm^3.
Its radius is 20 cm.
Work out its height.

7 A cylinder has volume 360π cm^3.
Its radius is 10 cm.
Work out its height.

8 The diagram shows a quadrant of a circle.
The radius is 8 cm.
a) Work out the area of the quadrant, in terms of π.
b) Work out the perimeter of the quadrant.
Give your answer correct to 3 significant figures.

9 The diagram shows an unusual carpet.
It is in the shape of a square, with semicircles on each of the four sides.
Each side of the square is 3.4 m.
a) Work out the area of one of the semicircles.
Leave your answer in terms of π.
b) Hence find the total area of the carpet.
Give your answer correct to 3 significant figures.

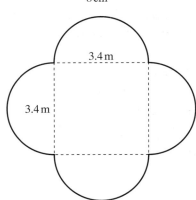

10 The diagram shows two cylinders.
Cylinder A has diameter 5 cm and height 12 cm.
Cylinder B has diameter 12 cm and height 5 cm.
a) Show that both cylinders have exactly the same curved surface area.
b) Work out the volume of each cylinder, leaving your answers in terms of π.
c) Which cylinder has the larger volume?

Cylinder A   **Cylinder B**

Constructions and loci

EXERCISE 19.1

Make accurate drawings of these triangles, stating which of the various combinations of information you have been given: SAS, ASA, SSS or SSA. If any triangles are ambiguous, draw both possibilities.

1 Draw triangle ABC with BC = 9 cm, AC = 7 cm, angle BCA = 72°.

2 Draw triangle PQR with PQ = 8 cm, angle RPQ = 43°, angle RQP = 70°.

3 Draw triangle KLM with KL = 5 cm, LM = 4 cm, angle KLM = 150°.

4 Draw triangle DEF with DE = 9 cm, EF = 5.5 cm, angle DEF = 58°.

5 Draw triangle EFG with EF = 4.2 cm, FG = 7.5 cm, EG = 10 cm.

6 Draw triangle JKL with JK = 8.1 cm, JL = 5 cm, LK = 5 cm.

7 The sketch shows a triangle with AB = 73 mm, BC = 56 mm, AC = 87 mm. Make an accurate drawing of this triangle.

8 The sketch shows a triangle with AB = 84 mm, BC = 52 mm and angle ACB = 90°. Make an accurate drawing of this triangle.

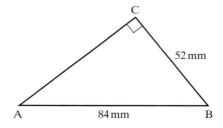

9 Draw triangle PQR with PQ = 8.1 cm, QR = 8.8 cm, angle RPQ = 90°.
Use ruler and compasses to construct this triangle.
Show that there are two different solutions based on the given information.

10 Using compasses, try to make an accurate construction of triangle EFG with sides EF = 14 cm, FG = 6 cm, EG = 7 cm. What difficulty do you encounter?
Find a reason for this.

EXERCISE 19.2

1 Use ruler and compasses to construct the perpendicular bisector of the line segment AB (AB is 7 cm long).

A————————————— B

2 Use ruler and compasses to construct the bisector of angle ABC.

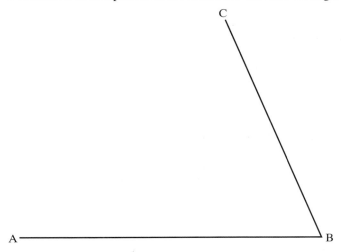

3 Use ruler and compasses to construct the perpendicular from A to the line segment PQ.

4 Use ruler and compasses to construct a line passing through X, perpendicular to the line AB.

5 Use ruler and compasses to construct the bisector of angle CDE.

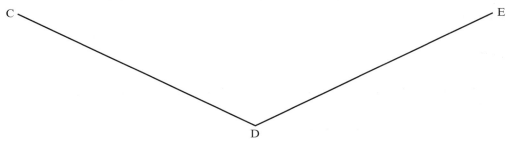

6 Use ruler and compasses to construct the perpendicular bisector of the line segment PQ (PQ is 9.6 cm long).

P ——————————————————————— Q

7 Use ruler and compasses to construct a line passing through ×, perpendicular to the line CD.

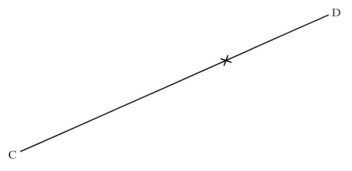

8 Use ruler and compasses to construct the perpendicular from P to the line segment AB.

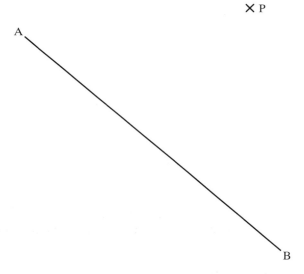

9 Using compasses and a straight edge draw an angle of exactly 150°.
Hint: Draw a line segment about 7 or 8 cm long – the exact length is unimportant.
Then use compasses and a straight edge to construct an equilateral triangle, using this segment as one side of the triangle. Take one of the angles and bisect it. This gives an angle of 30°.
Finally, extend one of the arms of the 30° angle.

10 Using compasses and a straight edge, construct an angle of exactly 135°.
Hint: Draw a line segment about 15 cm long. Construct the perpendicular bisector of the line. This gives an angle of 90°. Bisect the angle to give an angle of 45°. The 90° together with 45° gives 135°.

EXERCISE 19.3

1 In the diagram, the rectangle PQRS represents a farm. It is to be divided up into three regions.

The region formed by all points within 30 metres of PS will be the farm house.
The region formed by all points within 40 metres of Q will be the hen house.
The rest of the farm will be covered with grass.
On a copy of the diagram, indicate each of the three regions.

2 The diagram shows a paved play area at a school.

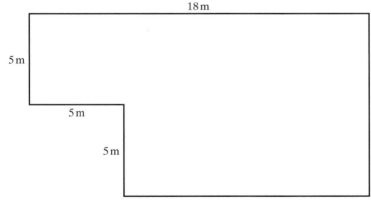

The local authority wants to erect a fence around the outside of the play area.
They decide that the fence should come to within 2 metres of the nearest point of the play area.
On a copy of the diagram, make a drawing to show the position of the fence.

3 The diagram shows a sketch of a rectangular nature reserve.
A gravel path is to be laid.
The centre line of the path runs diagonally from E to G.
All parts of the nature reserve within 1 metre of this centre line are to be gravelled.

a) Using a scale of 1 cm = 2 m, draw the rectangle.
b) Mark the centre line of the path.
c) Shade the region to be gravelled.

A pond is to be built in the nature reserve.
The pond will occupy all points within 4.6 m of F.
d) Shade the area where the pond will be.

4 At the edge of a bay there are three lighthouses.
The diagram shows the position of the three lighthouses, P, Q and R.

Land

a) Using compasses and a straight edge, construct the locus of all points that are equidistant from P and Q.

b) Repeat the construction using Q and R, and again, using P and R.

c) Hence divide the bay into three regions, one for each lighthouse.
Use coloured pencils to mark the regions distinctly.

5 The diagram shows a sketch of a rectangular field ABCD.
Harry wants to bury some treasure in the field.

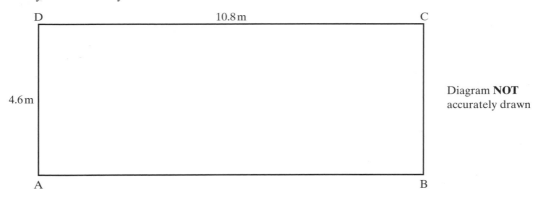

D   10.8 m   C

4.6 m

Diagram **NOT**
accurately drawn

A   B

a) Using a scale of 1 cm = 1 m, construct the rectangular field ABCD.

Harry buries the treasure exactly 3.5 m from DC, and exactly the same distance from AB and BC.

b) On a copy of the diagram, mark with a cross (✗) where Harry buried the treasure.

U3 CHAPTER 20

Transformation and similarity

EXERCISE 20.1

1 Diagram **a)** shows a 2-D shape. Copy the diagram and draw a line of symmetry on your diagram.

Diagram **b)** shows a sketch of a 3-D object. Copy the diagram and indicate a plane of symmetry on your sketch.

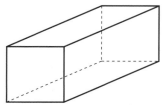

a)

b)

In questions **2** to **5**, copy the diagram and draw the reflection of the given shape in the mirror line indicated. Label each mirror line with its equation.

2

3

4

5

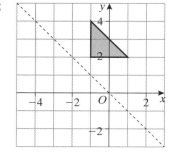

6 The diagram shows a triangle P and its mirror image Q.
   a) Copy the diagram and draw the mirror line that has been used for the reflection.
   b) Write down the equation of the mirror line.

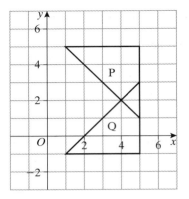

7 The diagram shows a triangle S and its mirror image T.
   a) Copy the diagram and draw the mirror line that has been used for the reflection.
   b) Write down the equation of the mirror line.

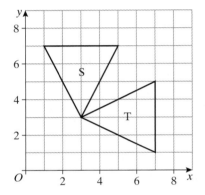

8 The diagram shows a letter T shape, labelled X. The shape is to be reflected in a mirror line. Part of the reflection has been drawn on the diagram.

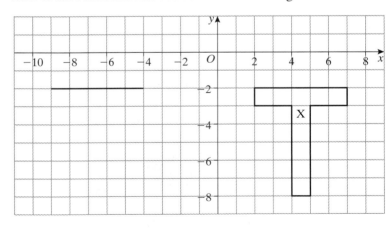

   a) Copy the diagram and complete the drawing to show the image. Label it Y.
   b) Mark the mirror line and give its equation.

⚙✸   **20 Transformation and similarity U3**

9 The diagram shows ten triangles A to J.
The ten triangles are all congruent to
each other.

a) Explain the meaning of the word
congruent.

b) Triangle E can be reflected to
triangle I. State the equation of the
mirror line that achieves this.

c) Triangle H is reflected to another
triangle using the mirror line $x = -1\frac{1}{2}$.
Which one?

d) Triangle D can be reflected to
triangle E using a mirror line.
Give the equation of this line.

e) Triangle B can be reflected to
triangle E using a mirror line.
Give the equation of this line.

f) Triangle A can be reflected to
triangle C using a mirror line.
Give the equation of this line.

g) Triangle G is reflected to another
triangle using the mirror line $y = -3$. Which one?

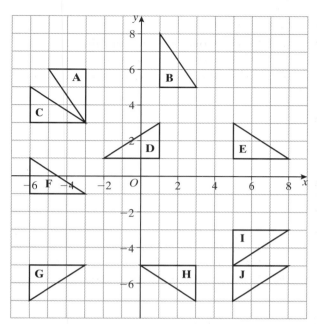

10 A triangle P is reflected in the line $x = 3$ to form an image, triangle Q.
Then triangle Q is reflected in the same mirror line to form an image, triangle R.
What can you deduce about triangle P and triangle R?

EXERCISE 20.2

For each of questions **1** to **6**, copy the diagram on to a coordinate grid on which x and y range
from -8 to 8.

1 Rotate the trapezium shape
90° clockwise about O.

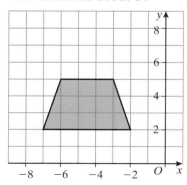

2 Rotate the L-shape 180° about O.

3

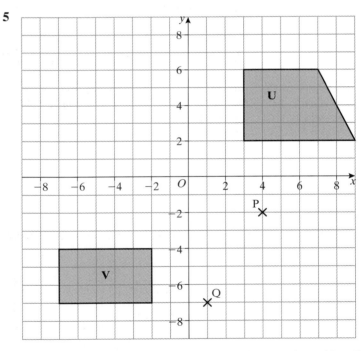

a) Rotate the triangle T1 90° anticlockwise about *O*.
Label the result T2.

b) Rotate T2 180° about *O*.
Label the result T3.

c) Describe the single rotation that takes T1 directly to T3.

4

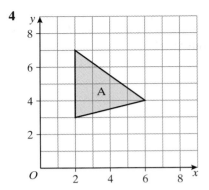

a) Rotate triangle A 90° anticlockwise about (0, 0).
Label the result B.

b) Rotate triangle B by 180° about (0, 0).
Label the result C.

c) Describe carefully the single rotation that takes triangle C to triangle A.

5

a) Rotate shape U 90° anticlockwise about point P (4, −2).

b) Rotate shape V 90° clockwise about point Q (1, −7).

20 Transformation and similarity U3

6 a) Rotate triangle A 90° clockwise about (1, 1). Label it B.

b) Now rotate both triangle A and triangle B by 180° about (1, 1).

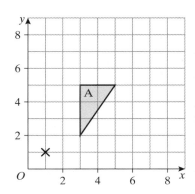

7 The diagram shows an object A and its image B after a rotation.

a) Write down the size and direction of the angle of rotation.

b) Write down the coordinates of the centre of rotation.

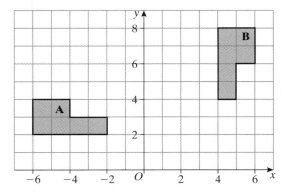

8 Mel says, 'If you translate a shape and then translate it again, the result is equivalent to a single translation.'

Joe says, 'If you reflect a shape and then reflect it again, the result is equivalent to a single reflection.'

Emily says, 'I'm afraid only one of you is right.'

Who is right, and who is wrong?

EXERCISE 20.3

For each of questions **1** to **6**, copy the diagram on to a coordinate grid on which *x* and *y* range from −8 to 8.

1 a) Reflect triangle S in the line *x* = −1.
Label the new triangle T.

b) Reflect triangle T in the *x* axis.
Label the new triangle U.

c) Describe the **single** transformation that maps S to U.

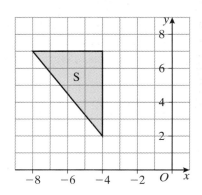

2 The diagram shows a triangle, T.

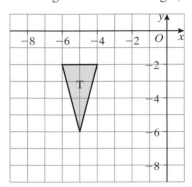

a) Translate triangle T by $\begin{pmatrix} 0 \\ 4 \end{pmatrix}$.

Label its image U.

b) Rotate triangle U by 90° clockwise about O. Label the resulting triangle V.

c) Describe the single transformation that maps T to V.

3 The diagram shows a triangle, S.

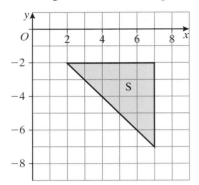

a) Reflect triangle S in the y axis. Label its image T.

b) Reflect triangle T in the line $y = -2$. Label its image U.

c) Describe the single transformation that maps S directly to U.

4 The diagram shows a letter F shape. The shape is labelled F1.

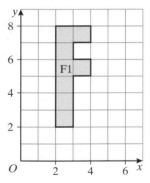

a) Reflect F1 in the y axis. Label the image F2.

b) Reflect F2 in the line $y = x$. Label this image F3.

c) Describe the single transformation that would take F3 to F1.

5 The diagram shows a quadrilateral E.

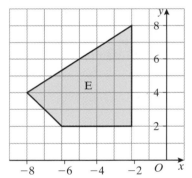

a) Rotate quadrilateral E through 90° anticlockwise about O. Label the result F.

b) Rotate quadrilateral F through 90° clockwise about $(1, -1)$. Label the result G.

c) Describe a single transformation that would take G to E.

20 Transformation and similarity U3

6 The diagram shows a triangle P.

   a) Rotate triangle P 90° anticlockwise about (0, 1).
Label this result Q.

   b) Translate triangle P by the vector $\begin{pmatrix} 9 \\ 5 \end{pmatrix}$.
Label this result R.

   c) Describe the single transformation that transforms
triangle R to triangle Q.

EXERCISE 20.4

1 Copy the diagram showing shape A and point P onto a
coordinate grid on which x and y range from 0 to 18.

   a) Enlarge shape A by scale factor 2, centre P.
Label the new shape B.

   b) Enlarge shape A by scale factor 3, centre P.
Label the new shape C.

   c) Are shapes B and C:

      (i) congruent   **(ii)** similar?

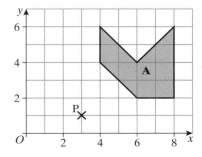

2 Copy the triangle, and a centre of enlargement P, onto a
coordinate grid on which x ranges from 0 to 18 and y ranges
from 0 to 10.

   Enlarge the triangle by scale factor −2, centre P.

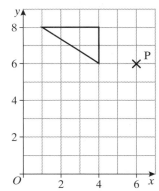

3 Draw the trapezium on a coordinate grid on which x and y
range from −10 to 10.
Add the centre of enlargement P at (6, −8).

   Enlarge the shape by scale factor $2\frac{1}{2}$, centre P.

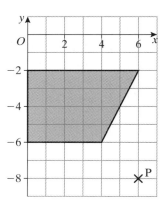

4 On a coordinate grid on which x ranges from 0 to 26 and y ranges from -2 to 16, draw shape P and centres A and B.

a) Enlarge shape P, with scale factor 3, centre A (2, 4). Label the result Q.

b) Enlarge shape Q, with scale factor $\frac{1}{3}$, centre B (14, -2). Label the result R.

c) State whether shapes P and Q are
(i) congruent   (ii) similar.

d) Are shapes P and R congruent?

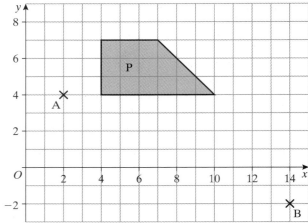

5 The diagram shows an object, A, and its image B after an enlargement.

a) State the scale factor for the enlargement.

b) Obtain the coordinates of the centre of enlargement.

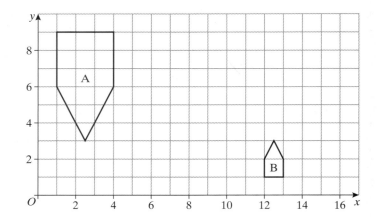

6 Ned draws a triangle and then enlarges it.
He notices that the image of the triangle is congruent to the original triangle.

a) What scale factor do you think Ned has used?

b) What other transformation could Ned have used to get the same result?

 EXERCISE 20.5

1 The diagram shows two triangles.
They are mathematically similar.

a) Work out the height of the larger triangle.

b) Work out the ratio of the perimeters of the triangles, in the form $1 : n$.

c) Find the ratio of the areas of the triangles, in the form $1 : n$.

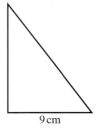

20 Transformation and similarity U3

2 The diagram shows two similar parallelograms.
The smaller parallelogram has an area of 34 cm².
Work out the area of the larger parallelogram.

10 cm   25 cm

3 The diagram shows two solid cylinders.
They are similar.
Both cylinders are made of the same material.
The larger cylinder has a mass of 24.576 kg.
Work out the mass of the smaller cylinder.

2.4 m   1.5 m

4 In the diagram, AB and CD are parallel.

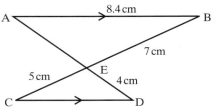
8.4 cm
A   B
7 cm
E
5 cm
4 cm
C   D

a) **(i)** Work out the length of AE.
(ii) Hence find the length of AD.
b) Calculate the length of CD.

5 A shop has two dolls' houses.
They are mathematically similar.
One of the dolls' houses is 50% larger than the other one.
The smaller dolls' house has a length of 76 cm and a mass of 6 kg.
a) Calculate the length of the larger dolls' house.
The two dolls' houses are made from the same materials.
b) Calculate the mass of the larger dolls' house.

6 In the diagram, PQ and ST are parallel.
Calculate the lengths x and y.

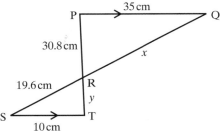
35 cm
P   Q
30.8 cm
x
19.6 cm   R
y
S   T
10 cm

7 Bill makes two similar garden gnomes.
The smaller one is 24 cm tall and weighs 1.6 kg.
The larger one is 40 cm tall.
Work out the weight of the larger garden gnome.

8 The diagram shows triangle ABC and triangle ADE.
The line segments DE and BC are parallel.
AD = 10 cm, AE = 9 cm, DE = 15 cm, BC = 20 cm.
a) Explain fully why triangles ABC and ADE are similar.
b) Work out the length AC.   **c)** Work out the length BD.

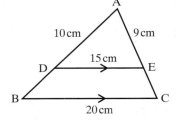
A
10 cm   9 cm
D   15 cm   E
B   20 cm   C

9 An architect builds a large model of a new school building she has designed.
The height of the model is 0.6 m and the model covers an area of 5 m².
The new school building will be mathematically similar to the model but 20 times larger.
Calculate: **a)** the height of the new school building; **b)** the area the new school will cover.

10 Two buckets are mathematically similar.
The height of the smaller bucket is 30 cm and it can hold 4 litres of water.
The larger bucket holds 8 litres of water.
Calculate the height of the larger bucket. Give your answer correct to 1 decimal place.

Pythagoras' theorem

EXERCISE 21.1

Look at these triangles, and use Pythagoras' theorem to decide whether they are right-angled or not. The diagrams are not drawn to scale.

1
5 cm   6 cm
8.5 cm

2
4 m   5 m
6 m

3
15 mm
9 mm
12 mm

For each of the triangles described below, use Pythagoras' theorem to decide whether it is right-angled. If so, name the angle at which the right angle is located.

4 AB = 9 cm, BC = 7 cm, CA = 5.4 cm.   **5** AB = 2.5 cm, BC = 1.5 cm, CA = 2 cm.

6 AB = 8 mm, BC = 8 mm, CA = 11 mm.   **7** PQ = 2.6 cm, QR = 3.5 cm, RS = 5 cm.

8 PQ = 2.5 m, QR = 6 m, RS = 6.5 m.   **9** PQ = 7.2 cm, QR = 8.3 cm, RS = 12 cm.

10 AB = 15 km, BC = 20 km, CA = 25 km.

EXERCISE 21.2

In questions **1** to **9**, find the length of the hypotenuse represented by the letters *a* to *i*. Give your answers to 3 significant figures where appropriate.

1
3 cm   *a*
7 cm

2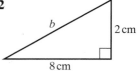
b   2 cm
8 cm

3
5.2 m   6.3 m
c

4
d   1.6 km
2.1 km

5
4.7 mm   *e*
2.8 mm

6
f   9.3 cm
6.7 cm

7
15 km
11 km
g

8
h
5 mm   8.7 mm

9
0.6 m
0.26 m   *i*

Find the length of the diagonal of each rectangle.

10
x
4 m
7 m

11
y
4.8 cm
3.1 cm

12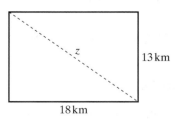
z
13 km
18 km

EXERCISE 21.3

Find the length of the side marked by the letters a to i below.
Give your answers to 3 significant figures where appropriate.

1
12 cm
a
8 cm

2
7 m
b
5 m

3
4 cm
11 cm
c

4
20 cm
12 cm
d

5
9 mm
13 mm
e

6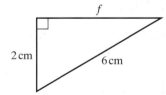
f
2 cm
6 cm

7
7.3 cm
g
4.8 cm

8
9.5 m
h
12.3 m

9
0.7 m
0.3 m
i

10 A rectangle has length y cm and width 6 cm. Its diagonal is of length 6.5 cm.
Find the value of y.

11 A ship sails due West for x km and then sails due South for 20 km.
It ends up 25 km in a direct straight line from its starting point.
Find the value of x.

The last part of this exercise contains a mixture of questions. Remember to square and add when you are finding a hypotenuse, but square and subtract when finding a shorter side.
In both cases, remember to square root at the end.

In questions **12** to **15** find the length of the side marked by the letters *a* to *d*.
Give your answers to 3 significant figures where appropriate.

 # EXERCISE 21.4

Give all answers correct to 3 significant figures.

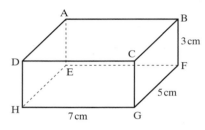

1 The diagram shows a box in the shape of a cuboid.
  a) Work out the length FH.
  b) Work out the length HB.

2 The diagram shows a box in the shape of a cuboid.
  a) Work out the length BD.
  b) Work out the length BH.

3 A cuboid measures 3 cm by 5 cm by 9 cm.
  a) Make a sketch of the cuboid.
  b) Calculate the length of the diagonal.

4 A box measures 8 cm by 13 cm by 18 cm.
Rob has a giant pencil of length 25 cm.
Use Pythagoras' theorem to explain whether it is possible to put Rob's pencil in the box so that it does not stick out of the box.

5 The diagram shows a wedge.
The rectangular face ABDE is at right angles to the rectangular face CBEF.
DE = 14 cm, EF = 6 cm, BE = 20 cm.
  a) Calculate the length BD.
  b) Calculate the direct distance from C to D.

6 A thin rod of length 15 cm just fits inside a cylindrical container of length 11 cm.
Find the diameter of the cylinder.

7 Find the length of the longest thin rod that will just fit inside a cuboid-shaped box with dimensions 6 cm by 8 cm by 26 cm.

U3 CHAPTER 22

Introducing trigonometry

EXERCISE 22.1

Work out the values of the sides represented by letters.
Round your answers correct to 3 significant figures.

1

2

3

4

5

6

7

8

9

10

11 In triangle ABC, BC = 20 cm, angle ABC = 90°, angle CAB = 35°. Calculate AC.

12 In triangle DEF, angle DEF = 90°, angle DFE = 74°, DE = 8.6 mm. Calculate DF.

13 In triangle GHJ, angle GHJ = 90°, angle GJH = 50°, GJ = 83 cm. Calculate GH.

14 In triangle KLM, angle KLM = 90°, angle LMK = 12°, KL = 9.4 mm. Calculate KM.

15 In triangle NPQ, angle NPQ = 90°, angle PNQ = 69°, NQ = 293 m. Calculate PQ.

EXERCISE 22.2

Work out the values of the sides represented by letters.
Give your answers correct to 3 significant figures.

1
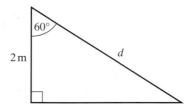
20 cm, 52°, *a*

2
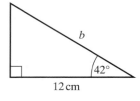
b, 42°, 12 cm

3

c, 25°, 5.6 cm

4

60°, 2 m, *d*

5

e, 15°, 5.2 cm

6
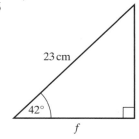
23 cm, 42°, *f*

7
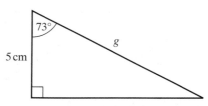
73°, 5 cm, *g*

8

h, 62°, 25 m

9

i, 18°, 63 cm

10
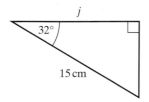
j, 32°, 15 cm

11 In triangle ABC, AC = 8.2 cm, angle ABC = 90°, angle ACB = 61°. Calculate BC.

12 In triangle DEF, angle DEF = 90°, angle FDE = 37°, DE = 9 cm. Calculate DF.

13 In triangle GHJ, angle GHJ = 90°, angle GJH = 56°, GJ = 125 m. Calculate HJ.

14 In triangle KLM, angle KLM = 90°, angle LKM = 23°, LK = 57 mm. Calculate KM.

15 In triangle NPQ, angle NPQ = 90°, angle PQN = 40°, NQ = 66.6 cm. Calculate PQ.

22 Introducing trigonometry U3

EXERCISE 22.3

Work out the values of the sides represented by letters.
Give your answers correct to 3 significant figures.

1
13°, 21 cm, *a*

2
b, 10 cm, 43°

3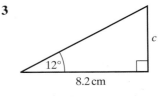
12°, 8.2 cm, *c*

4
10.3 m, *d*, 18°

5
e, 72°, 10 cm

6
f, 28°, 8 cm

7
g, 15 cm, 65°

8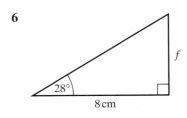
34 mm, *h*, 51°

9
32°, *i*, 60 cm

10
j, 8 m, 41°

11 In triangle ABC, BC = 20 cm, angle ABC = 90°, angle CAB = 23°. Calculate AB.

12 In triangle KLM, angle KLM = 90°, angle KML = 18°, KL = 11.4 cm. Calculate LM.

EXERCISE 22.4 pt

Work out the unknown lengths represented by letters.
Round your answers correct to 3 significant figures.

1
5 cm, *a*, 42°

2
48°, 4 cm, *b*

3
10 m, 38°, *c*

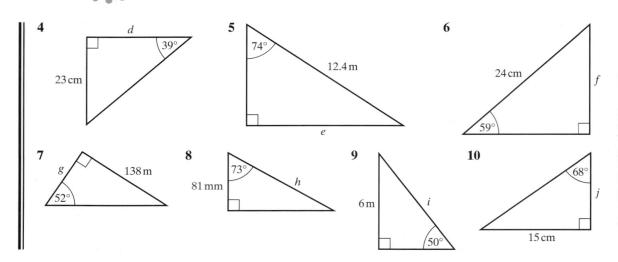

4 d, 39°, 23 cm

5 74°, 12.4 m, e

6 24 cm, f, 59°

7 g, 138 m, 52°

8 73°, 81 mm, h

9 6 m, i, 50°

10 68°, j, 15 cm

EXERCISE 22.5

Work out the values of the angles represented by letters.

Round your final answers correct 1 decimal place.

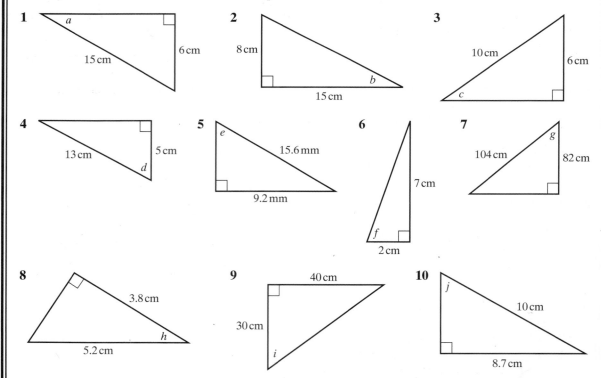

1 a, 15 cm, 6 cm

2 8 cm, 15 cm, b

3 10 cm, 6 cm, c

4 13 cm, 5 cm, d

5 e, 15.6 mm, 9.2 mm

6 7 cm, f, 2 cm

7 104 cm, g, 82 cm

8 3.8 cm, 5.2 cm, h

9 40 cm, 30 cm, i

10 j, 10 cm, 8.7 cm

11 In triangle ABC, angle ABC = 90°, AB = 18 cm, AC = 23 cm. Calculate angle ACB.

12 In triangle DEF, angle DEF = 90°, EF = 6.2 cm, DE = 4.3 cm. Calculate angle EFD.

EXERCISE 22.6 pt

1 A ship sails 27 km due South, then 16 km due West.
  a) Illustrate this information on a sketch.
  b) How far, to the nearest 0.1 km, is the ship from its starting point?
  c) What bearing, to the nearest degree, should it steer to return directly to its start point?

2 In the diagram, PRS is a straight line. PQ = 9.2 cm,
QS = 7.6 cm and angle QPR = 38°.
QR is perpendicular to PS.
  a) Calculate the length QR.
    Give your answer to 3 significant figures.
  b) Calculate angle QSP.
    Give your answer to the nearest 0.1 cm.
  c) Calculate angle PQS.
    Give your answer to the nearest 0.1°.

3 The diagram shows a cross section of a triangular prism.
AB = BC = 7 cm. BM = 5 cm.
M is the midpoint of the line segment AC.
  a) Explain why angle AMB must be a right angle.
  b) Calculate the angle BCM. Give your answer to the nearest 0.1°.
  c) Calculate the area of the triangle.
    Give your answer to 3 significant figures.

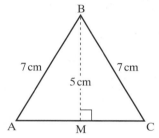

4 A 5 m ladder leans against a vertical wall. The bottom of the ladder is 2.8 m from the wall.
  a) Illustrate this information on a sketch.
  b) Calculate the angle between the ladder and the wall.
    Give your answer correct to 1 decimal place.
  c) Calculate how high the top of the ladder is above the ground.
    Give your answer to 3 significant figures.

5 In the diagram, EHG is a straight line. Angle EHF = 90°.
Angle FGH = 68°. EG = 26 cm, FH = 15 cm.
  a) Work out the length of GH, correct to 3 significant figures.
  b) Work out the size of angle FEH, correct to the
    nearest degree.

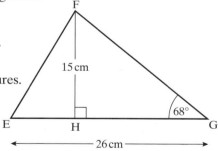

6 Annerly is due North of Carr and is 300 km away.
Bronwich is between Annerly and Carr.
Dinby is due West of Bronwich and is 123 km away.
The bearing of Dinby from Carr is 307°.
  a) Draw a sketch to show this information.
  b) Calculate the distance between Bronwich and Carr. Give your answer to 3 significant figures.
  c) How far north of Bronwich is Annerly? Give your answer to 4 significant figures.
  d) Work out the distance and bearing of Annerly from Dinby.

2-D and 3-D objects

EXERCISE 23.1

1 Find the sum of the interior angles of
  a) a hexagon
  b) a 10-sided polygon.

2 Work out the size of the exterior angle at each vertex of
  a) a regular pentagon
  b) a regular 12-sided polygon.

3 Seven of the angles in an octagon are 152°, 123°, 168°, 145°, 110°, 125° and 130°. Find the eighth angle.

4 a) The diagram shows part of a regular polygon.

Work out how many sides the polygon has.

  b) Emma draws this diagram. She says it shows part of a regular polygon.

Explain how you can tell that Emma must have made a mistake.

5 The diagram shows an irregular hexagon. Work out the value of the angle marked *h*.

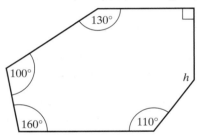

6 a) Work out the value of *x*.
  b) Hence work out the size of each angle.

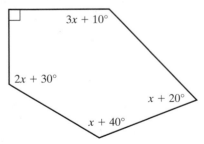

7 The diagram shows an octagon. All the angles marked *w* are equal. Calculate the value of *w*.

8 The diagram shows a pentagon. It has a vertical line of symmetry.

  a) Explain carefully why $a + b = 215°$.
     Angle a is 45° smaller than angle b.
  b) Use this information to rewrite the equation
     $a + b = 215°$ so it does not contain a.
     Solve this equation to find the value of b.
  c) Hence find the other angles in the pentagon.
  d) Julian says the pentagon is regular. Is he right? Explain your answer.

X EXERCISE 23.2

1 A cuboid measures 5 cm by 6 cm by 2 cm.
  a) Draw a sketch of the cuboid.
  b) Make an isometric drawing of the cuboid.
  c) Draw a net for the cuboid.

2 A pyramid is drawn on a rectangular base.
   The base is 4 cm by 5 cm. The pyramid is 8 cm tall.
  a) Draw a sketch of the pyramid.
  b) Draw a plan view, a front elevation and a side elevation.
  c) Draw an accurate net for the pyramid.

3 A triangular prism is 8 cm long. Its ends are equilateral triangles of side 5 cm.
  a) Draw a sketch of the prism.   **b)** Draw an accurate net for the prism.

4 The isometric drawing shows some cubes forming a 3-D shape.
  a) Copy the shape onto isometric paper.
  b) On squared paper draw a sketch of
     (i) a plan view as seen from **A**
     (ii) a side elevation as seen from **B**
     (iii) a front elevation, as seen from **C**.

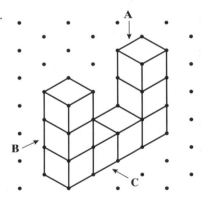

5 Kamini and Dakshesh have been building shapes with centimetre cubes on a square grid.
   The diagrams show plan views of their shapes.
   The numbers 1, 2, 3 tell you how many cubes are
   stacked on top of each square.
  a) Draw a front elevation to show how Kamini's
     shape appears seen from direction A.
  b) Make an isometric drawing of Dakshesh's shape,
     viewed from direction B.

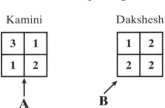

6 Here are three projections of a solid object.

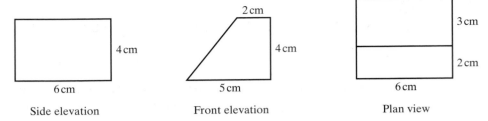

Side elevation   Front elevation   Plan view

     a) Make a sketch of the solid object.
     b) Make an isometric drawing of the solid object.

EXERCISE 23.3

Find the volume and total surface area of each of the solids in questions **1** to **6**.
Give your answers exactly, in terms of π.
Also give corresponding numerical values, correct to 3 significant figures.

1

←3 cm→

2

13 cm

←10 cm→

3

24 cm

←18 cm→

4

←5 cm→

5

←10 cm→

6

25 cm

←14 cm→

7 A pyramid has a square base of side 4 cm and a vertical height of 7 cm. Find its volume.

8 A square-based pyramid has a volume of 5000 cm³. Its height is 6 cm.
Find the dimensions of the base.

9 A sphere has surface area 484π cm². Find its volume in terms of π.

10 A cone of slant height 10 cm has a curved surface area of 50π cm².
Find the area of its base in terms of π.

EXERCISE 23.4

1 Convert 3.62 m³ into cm³.   2 Convert 280 mm² into cm².   3 Convert 200 000 m² into km².

4 Convert 3.85 cm³ into mm³.   5 Convert 490 000 mm² into m².

6 A pyramid has a volume of 2 600 000 mm³.   7 A cuboid has a surface area of 0.6 m².
   Express its volume in cm³.   Express its area in cm².

For questions **8** to **10**, you may use the information that 1 litre = 1000 cm³.

8 A bath contains 450 litres of water.
   a) Convert 450 litres into cm³.
   b) Hence find the amount of water in the bath in m³.

9 A water tank in the shape of a cuboid measures 2.3 m by 5.7 m by 3 m.
   a) Find the volume of the tank, in m³.
   b) Convert this answer into cm³.
   c) How many litres of water can the tank hold?

10 A tank in the shape of a cube has a capacity of 1331 litres.
   a) Express this capacity in cm³.
   b) Convert your answer to part **a)** into m³.
   c) Find the dimensions of the tank in metres.

EXERCISE 23.5

1 The table shows six expressions: p, q and r are lengths. 5 and 2 are numbers and have no
   dimension.

$p + 2q + r$	p^2q^2	$2rq^2$	$\dfrac{pr^2}{q}$	$5pqr$	$2p(r + 5q)$

   a) Copy the table and put the letter A in the box underneath each of the **two** expressions that
           could represent an **area**.
   b) Put the letter V in the box underneath each of the **two** expressions that could represent a
           volume.

2 Here are three expressions.

Expression	Length	Area	Volume	None of these
$3\pi x + \pi y^2$				
$\pi z^2 + 2y^2$				
$\pi x^2 y$				

x, y and z are lengths. π and 3 are numbers and have no dimensions.

Copy the grid and put a tick ($\checkmark$) in the correct column to show whether the expression can be used for length, area, volume or none of these.

3 The expressions below can be used to calculate lengths, areas or volumes of some shapes. The letters b, w and h represent lengths. π and 3 are numbers and have no dimension.
Pick out the **three** expressions that can be used to calculate a **volume**.

$bh + 3w$ $\qquad \dfrac{\pi}{3}bwh \qquad \dfrac{bh}{3} \qquad \dfrac{w^2h^2}{b} \qquad \pi b^2h^2$

$\pi h(b^2 + 3wh) \qquad \pi bh \qquad 3\pi(bw + wh) \qquad bh(\pi + 3) \qquad 3b^2 + 3bh$

4 Here are three expressions.

Expression	Length	Area	Volume	None of these
$6\pi b(2a + c)$				
$\dfrac{3ac}{\pi b}$				
$\pi a^2 + 2\pi b$				

a, b and c are lengths. π, 2, 3 and 6 are numbers and have no dimensions.
Copy the grid and put a tick ($\checkmark$) in the correct column to show whether the expression can be used for length, area, volume or none of these.

5 Here are some expressions. The letters x, y, z and h represent lengths.
π and 10 are numbers that have no dimensions.
Three of the expressions could represent areas.
Copy the grid and tick ($\checkmark$) the boxes underneath the three expressions which could represent areas.

$\pi(x + y + z)$	$10\pi xh$	$\pi x(10h + z)$	y^2z	$\dfrac{\pi x^2 h}{y}$	$10y^3z$	$\dfrac{\pi yz}{x}$

EXERCISE 23.6 pt

1 A square has sides of length 9 cm, correct to the nearest centimetre.
   a) Calculate the upper and lower bounds for the perimeter of the square.
   b) Calculate the upper and lower bounds for the area of the square.

2 A rectangle has a length of 5.3 cm (rounded to 2 significant figures) and a width of 2.15 cm (rounded to 3 significant figures).
   a) Calculate the upper bound for the perimeter of the rectangle.
   b) Calculate the lower bound for the area of the rectangle.

3 To 1 decimal place, $x = 21.3$ and $y = 5.6$.
   a) Calculate the upper bound for the value of xy.
   b) Calculate the lower bound for the value of $\dfrac{x}{y}$.
   Write down all the numbers on your calculator display.

4 A cylinder has a radius of 5 cm and a height of 12 cm, both correct to the nearest centimetre. Calculate the maximum volume of the cylinder.

5 A = 12.2 (rounded to 1 decimal place)
   B = 200 (rounded to the nearest hundred)
   C = 8 (rounded to the nearest whole number)

   a) Calculate the lower bound for A + B.
   b) Calculate the upper bound for B ÷ C.
   c) Calculate the maximum value of AC.
   d) Calculate the least value of $\dfrac{A + B}{B + C}$.

U3 CHAPTER 24

Circle theorems

EXERCISE 24.1

1 PT is a tangent to the circle, centre O.
PT = 12 cm. OP = 5 cm.
The line OT intersects the circle at R, as shown.
Work out the length of RT.

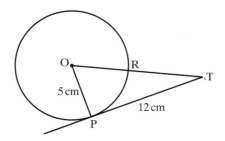

2 PQ is a tangent to the circle, centre O.
OP = 5 cm, OQ = 12 cm.
a) State the value of angle OPQ.
b) Calculate the length of PQ.

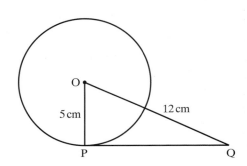

3 The diagram shows a circle, centre O.
The chord AB is 24 cm.
M is the midpoint of AB.
OM = 7 cm.

Calculate the length of the radius of the circle.

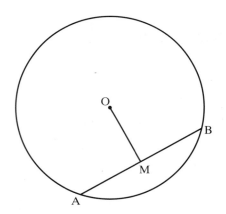

4 The diagram shows a circle, centre O, radius 30 cm.
PQ = 48 cm.
OM is perpendicular to PQ.

Work out the length of OM.

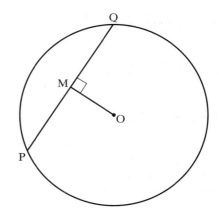

5 The diagram shows a circle, centre O. AB and CD are chords.
The diameter PQ passes through the midpoints M and N
of the chords.
OM =7 cm, AB = 10 cm and CD = 13 cm.

a) Explain why angle OMB = 90°.
b) Use Pythagoras' theorem to calculate the
distance OB. Show your working.
c) Calculate the distance MN.

EXERCISE 24.2

Find the missing angles *a* to *z* in these diagrams, which are not drawn to scale.
O is the centre of each circle.
Explain your reasoning in each case.

1

2

3

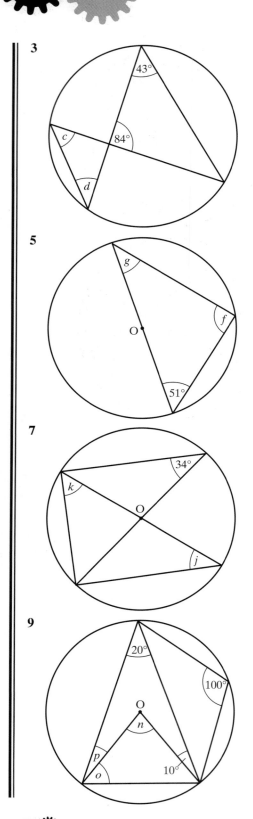

4

5

6

7

8

9

10

24 Circle theorems U3

11

3s

2s

O

12

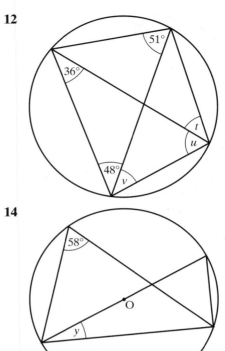

51°

36°

t

u

48°

v

13

w

O

x

50°

14

58°

O

y

15

z

O

33°

EXERCISE 24.3

Find the missing angles *a* to *z* in these diagrams, which are not drawn to scale.
O is the centre of the circle.
Explain your reasoning in each case.

1

2

3

4

5

6

7

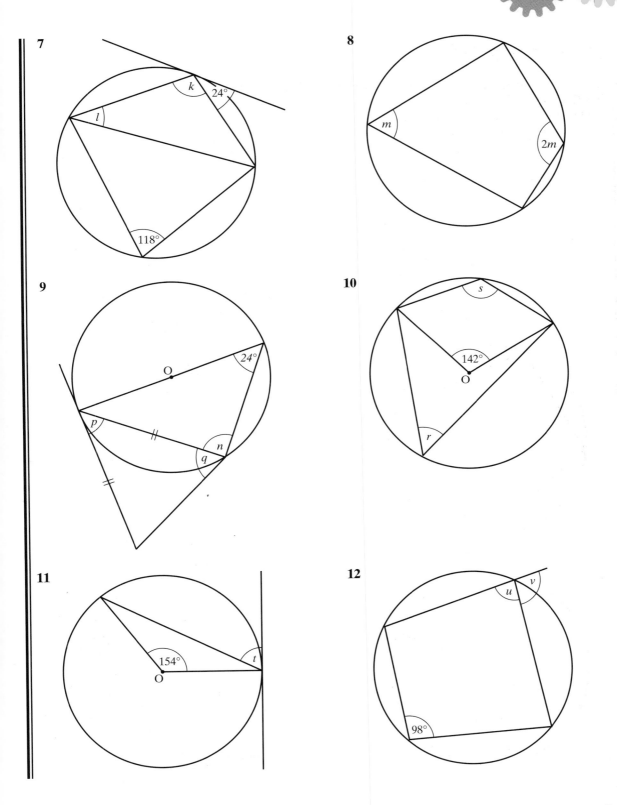

8

9

10

11

12

13

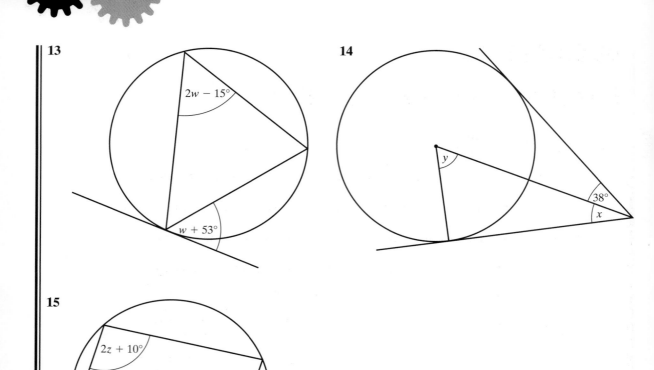

$2w - 15°$

$w + 53°$

14

y

$38°$

x

15

$2z + 10°$

$154°$

U3 CHAPTER 25

Direct and inverse proportion

EXERCISE 25.1

1 y is directly proportional to x, and $y = 8$ when $x = 10$. Find the value of y when $x = 15$.

2 y is directly proportional to x, and $y = 20$ when $x = 6$. Find x when $y = 50$.

3 Each of the tables below shows a set of matching x and y values, where y is directly proportional to x.
Find a formula for y in terms of x, and work out the missing values in each case.

a)

x	2	8	10
y	6	24	

b)

x	1		5	20
y		20		100

c)

x	8	24	
y		6	11

d)

x	7		70	84
y	3	9		

4 y is directly proportional to x, and it is known that $y = 14$ when $x = 35$.
a) Obtain an equation for y in terms of x.
b) Use your equation to find the values of:
  (i) y, when $x = 42$ **(ii)** x, when $y = 60$.

5 y is directly proportional to the square root of x, and $y = 28$ when $x = 16$.
Find y when $x = 400$.

6 y is directly proportional to x^2, and it is known that $y = 36$ when $x = 3$.
a) Obtain an equation for y in terms of x.
b) Use your equation to find the values of:
  (i) y, when $x = 10$ **(ii)** x, when $y = 100$.

7 y is directly proportional to x^3 and $y = 8$ when $x = 1$. Find y when $x = 6$.

8 Jason has a box of cylindrical shapes all made from the same material.
The shapes are of different sizes.
The weight, W grams, of each of these shapes varies as the cube of the length (x cm) of one of its sides.
One of the shapes has a length of 3 cm and a weight of 108 grams.
a) Find a formula for W in terms of x.
b) Work out the weight of a shape with length 6.5 cm.
c) One of the shapes weighs 2.916 kg. Work out the length of this shape.

9 Pierre sells jeans. His selling price, S, is directly proportional to the square of his cost price, C.
   Pierre bought 30 pairs of jeans for £600 and sold each pair for £50.
   a) Find a formula that Pierre can use to work out his selling price from his cost price.
   b) Pierre buys 40 pairs of designer jeans for £1200.
       Use the formula to work out his selling price for each of these pairs of designer jeans.

10 The time, T seconds, of each swing of a simple pendulum varies directly as the square root of its
   length, L cm.
   Chanelle has a 25 cm long pendulum that has a swing time of 1 second.
   Robert has a pendulum that is four times as long as Chanelle's pendulum.
   Calculate the swing time of Robert's pendulum.

EXERCISE 25.2

1 y is inversely proportional to x, and $y = 40$ when $x = 2$.
   Find the value of y when $x = 5$.

2 y is inversely proportional to x, and $y = 5$ when $x = 3$.
   Find x when $y = 3$.

3 Each of the tables below shows a set of matching x and y values, where y is inversely
   proportional to x.
   Find a formula for y in terms of x, and work out the missing values in each case.

a)

x	1		5
y	20	10	

b)

x	6	10	
y		24	16

c)

x	2		10
y		0.5	0.2

d)

x		5		20
y	5	2	1	

4 P is inversely proportional to Q, and $P = 12$ when $Q = 12$.
   a) Obtain an equation for P in terms of Q.
   b) Use your equation to find the values of:
       (i) Q, when $P = 36$
       (ii) P, when $Q = 9$.

5 R is inversely proportional to s, and it is known that $R = 9$ when $s = 40$.
   a) Obtain an equation for R in terms of s.
   b) Use your equation to find the values of:
       (i) R, when $s = 60$
       (ii) s, when $R = 18$.

6 y is inversely proportional to the cube of x, and $y = 25$ when $x = 2$. Find y when $x = 5$.

7 y is inversely proportional to x^2, and $y = 9$ when $x = 3$. Find x when $y = 81$.

8 The electrical resistance, R ohms, of a wire of given length is inversely proportional to the square of the diameter, d mm, of the wire.
When the diameter of the wire is 5 mm the resistance is 0.68 ohms.
  a) Find a formula for R in terms of d.
  b) Find the resistance of a wire with a diameter of 10 mm.

9 The volume, V cm^3, of a gas is inversely proportional to its pressure, P cm of mercury.
When the volume is 100 cm^3, the pressure is 54 cm of mercury.
  a) Calculate the volume when the pressure is 18 cm of mercury.
  b) Calculate the pressure when the volume is 270 cm^3.

10 Fred has a car showroom. He decides that the selling price, £S, of each car in the showroom will be inversely proportional to the square root of the age, A years, of the car. He sells a 9-year-old car for £900.
  a) Work out the selling price of a 4-year-old car.
  b) What is the **difference** in selling price between a 1-year-old car and a 2-year-old car?
  Give your answer correct to the nearest £.

EXERCISE 25.3

Copy these six sketch-graphs into your book.
Alongside each, write either 'Direct proportion', 'Inverse proportion' or 'Neither'.

1

2

3

4

5

6

U3 CHAPTER 26

Quadratic equations

Solve each of these quadratic equations by using the factorisation method.

1 $x^2 + 9x + 14 = 0$ **2** $x^2 + 19x + 60 = 0$ **3** $x^2 + x - 12 = 0$

4 $x^2 + 5x - 14 = 0$ **5** $x^2 + x - 30 = 0$ **6** $x^2 - 6x + 8 = 0$

7 $x^2 - 3x - 40 = 0$ **8** $x^2 - 12x + 35 = 0$ **9** $x^2 - 6x - 27 = 0$

10 $x^2 - x - 42 = 0$ **11** $2x^2 - 11x + 12 = 0$ **12** $3x^2 - 13x - 10 = 0$

13 $3x^2 + 8x + 4 = 0$ **14** $3x^2 + 2x - 16 = 0$ **15** $3x^2 + 13x + 4 = 0$

16 $2x^2 - 7x + 3 = 0$ **17** $2x^2 - 21x + 10 = 0$ **18** $5x^2 - 17x + 6 = 0$

19 $6x^2 + 17x + 12 = 0$ **20** $4x^2 + 7x + 3 = 0$

Here are some more difficult quadratic equations. Solve them by the factorisation method.

21 $4x^2 + 17x - 15 = 0$ **22** $6x^2 + 7x = 0$ **23** $25x^2 - 1 = 0$

24 $6x^2 + 9x = 0$ **25** $9x^2 - 12x + 4 = 0$ **26** $8x^2 - 2x = 0$

27 $6x^2 - 19x + 10 = 0$ **28** $20x^2 - 3x - 56 = 0$ **29** $9x^2 + 18x + 8 = 0$

30 $100 - 9x^2 = 0$

Rearrange these quadratic equations so that the right-hand side is zero. Then solve them by factorisation.

31 $2x^2 + x = 1$ **32** $x^2 + 24 = 10x$ **33** $x^2 + 19x = 11x + 20$

34 $x^2 + 7x = 2x + 6$ **35** $2x^2 = 7x - 3$ **36** $5 + 19x = 4x^2$

37 $6 = 7x + 5x^2$ **38** $3x^2 = 10x + 8$ **39** $6x^2 + 40x = 9x - 5$

40 $7x^2 = 44x - 12$

EXERCISE 26.2

Solve these equations using the quadratic equation formula.
Give your answers correct to 3 significant figures.

1 $x^2 + 4x + 2 = 0$ **2** $x^2 + 5x + 3 = 0$ **3** $2x^2 + 3x - 4 = 0$

4 $4x^2 - x - 4 = 0$ **5** $x^2 - 4x - 7 = 0$ **6** $2x^2 - 3x - 7 = 0$

7 $3x^2 - 8x + 2 = 0$ **8** $7x^2 + 8x - 2 = 0$ **9** $x^2 - 5x + 2 = 0$

10 $x^2 + 7x + 5 = 0$

Rearrange the equations below so that they are in the form $ax^2 + bx + c = 0$.
Then solve them using the formula method. Give your answers correct to 3 significant figures.

11 $5x^2 + 6x = 3$ **12** $x^2 + 2 = 4x$ **13** $2x^2 = 3x + 6$

14 $x(2x + 5) = 10$ **15** $2x(x - 1) = 5$ **16** $x^2 + x = 1$

17 $8x - 6 = x^2$ **18** $3x^2 = 20 + 2x$ **19** $2x^2 = 10 - 3x$

20 $4 + 2x = 7x^2$

EXERCISE 26.3

1 Two whole numbers y and $y + 3$ are multiplied together. The result is 108.
    a) Write down an equation in y.
    b) Show that this equation can be expressed as $y^2 + 3y - 108 = 0$.
    c) Solve the equation, to find the values of the two whole numbers.

2 The diagram shows a triangle.
   Its base is $(4x - 6)$ cm and its height is $3x$ cm.
   Its area is 105 cm^2.
    a) Write down an equation in x.
    b) Show that this equation can be expressed as
       $2x^2 - 3x - 35 = 0$.
    c) x is a whole number. Solve the equation to find the
       value of x.
    d) Hence find the base and height of the triangle.

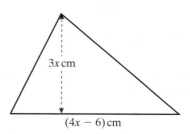

3 Chris and Hajra each thought of a positive whole number. Chris's number was 4 more than
   Hajra's number. Let Hajra's number be represented by x.
    a) Their two numbers multiply together to make 320. Write down an equation in x.
    b) Show that this equation can be expressed as $x^2 + 4x - 320 = 0$.
    c) Solve the equation, and hence find the numbers that Hajra and Chris thought of.

4 Two squares are drawn. One square has sides x cm long. The other square has sides 4 cm longer. The total area of **both** the squares is 208 cm².
   a) Write down an equation in x.
   b) Show that this equation can be expressed as $x^2 + 4x - 96 = 0$.
   c) Solve the equation to find the value of x.

5 The area of a rectangle is 40 cm².
   One side of the rectangle measures x cm and the other measures $(x + 3)$ cm.
   a) Express this information as an equation in x.
   b) Show that this equation can be expressed as $x^2 + 3x - 40 = 0$.
   c) Solve your equation, and hence find the dimensions of the rectangle.

6 A rectangle measures x cm by $(x + 5)$ cm.
   A second rectangle measures $(2x - 5)$ cm by $(x + 8)$ cm.
   a) Write down expressions for the areas of the two rectangles.
   Both rectangles have the same area.
   b) Show that $x^2 + 6x - 40 = 0$.
   c) Solve this equation.
   d) Hence determine the dimensions of each rectangle.

 EXERCISE 26.4

1 Write the following expressions in the form $(x + a)^2 + b$, giving the values of a and b:
   a) $x^2 + 6x + 10$ **b)** $x^2 + 2x + 5$

2 Write the expression $x^2 - 4x + 8$ in the form $(x + p)^2 + q$, giving the values of p and q.

3 Write the expression $x^2 - 10x - 15$ in the form $(x + f)^2 + g$, giving the values of f and g.

4 Write the expression $x^2 + 8x + 20$ in the form $(x + a)^2 + b$, giving the values of a and b.

5 a) Write the expression $x^2 - 20x + 10$ in the form $(x + a)^2 + b$, giving the values of a and b.
   b) Sketch the graph of $y = x^2 - 20x + 10$, marking the coordinates of the minimum point on the curve.

6 a) Write the expression $x^2 + 12x + 5$ in the form $(x + a)^2 + b$, giving the values of a and b.
   b) Sketch the graph of $y = x^2 + 12x + 5$, marking the coordinates of the minimum point on the curve.

7 a) Write the expression $x^2 - 2x - 7$ in the form $(x + a)^2 + b$, giving the values of a and b.
   b) Sketch the graph of $y = x^2 - 2x - 7$, marking the coordinates of the minimum point on the curve.

8 a) Write the expression $x^2 + 14x + 100$ in the form $(x + a)^2 + b$, giving the values of a and b.
   b) Sketch the graph of $y = x^2 + 14x + 100$, marking the coordinates of the minimum point on the curve.

9 a) Use the method of completing the square to help you sketch the graph of the function $y = x^2 + 30x + 20$.
   b) The graph has a vertical line of symmetry. Give the equation of this line.

U3 CHAPTER 27

Advanced algebra

EXERCISE 27.1

Simplify the following surds.

1 $\sqrt{20}$ **2** $\sqrt{75}$ **3** $\sqrt{27}$ **4** $\sqrt{32}$ **5** $\sqrt{28}$ **6** $\sqrt{54}$ **7** $\sqrt{500}$ **8** $\sqrt{72}$

Write each of these as a single surd term.

9 $\sqrt{50} + \sqrt{8}$

10 $\sqrt{40} + \sqrt{90}$

11 $\sqrt{300} - \sqrt{48}$

12 $\sqrt{80} + \sqrt{125}$

13 $\sqrt{7} + \sqrt{63}$

14 $\sqrt{44} - \sqrt{11}$

Simplify each of these.   **15** $\sqrt{5}(\sqrt{5} - \sqrt{7})$

16 $(5 + \sqrt{2})(3 - \sqrt{2})$

17 $(\sqrt{6} + \sqrt{5})(\sqrt{6} - \sqrt{5})$

18 $(5 - \sqrt{3})^2$

19 $\dfrac{\sqrt{27} + \sqrt{12}}{\sqrt{12}}$

20 A rectangle measures $(3 + \sqrt{44})$ cm long by $(6 - \sqrt{11})$ cm wide.
   a) Write the length of the rectangle in its simplest form.
   b) Work out the perimeter of the rectangle.
       Give your answer as an exact surd, in its simplest form.
   c) Work out the area of the rectangle.
       Give your answer as an exact surd, in its simplest form.

Solve each of the following quadratic equations, using the quadratic formula.
Leave your answers in surd form.

21 $x^2 + 5x + 2 = 0$

22 $x^2 - x - 1 = 0$

23 $x^2 - 8x + 3 = 0$

24 $x^2 - 8x + 5 = 0$

25 $2x^2 + 5x + 1 = 0$

EXERCISE 27.2

Express each of these as a single fraction.

1 $\dfrac{x}{2} + \dfrac{x + 4}{3}$

2 $\dfrac{x - 2}{3} + \dfrac{x + 5}{4}$

3 $\dfrac{2x}{7} + \dfrac{x + 3}{5}$

4 $\dfrac{x + 3}{2} - \dfrac{x + 1}{5}$

5 $\dfrac{5x + 3}{4} + \dfrac{x}{7}$

6 $\dfrac{3x - 1}{5} + \dfrac{x - 2}{2}$

7 $\dfrac{6}{x} + \dfrac{5}{x - 2}$

8 $\dfrac{1}{x - 4} + \dfrac{3}{x - 2}$

9 $\dfrac{5}{x - 2} + \dfrac{3}{x + 3}$

10 $\dfrac{4}{x+5} + \dfrac{3}{x+2}$

11 $\dfrac{7}{x+1} - \dfrac{3}{x+2}$

12 $\dfrac{3}{x+1} + \dfrac{2}{(x+1)(x+3)}$

Solve these equations involving algebraic fractions.

13 $\dfrac{x}{4} - \dfrac{x+2}{5} = 2$

14 $\dfrac{x+2}{2} + \dfrac{x-1}{5} = \dfrac{1}{10}$

15 $\dfrac{x-1}{3} = \dfrac{x+1}{4}$

16 $\dfrac{4x+1}{3} - \dfrac{3}{2} = \dfrac{2x+5}{6}$

17 $\dfrac{2x-3}{6} + \dfrac{x+2}{3} = \dfrac{5}{2}$

18 $\dfrac{3}{2x} + \dfrac{1}{x} = \dfrac{2}{5}$

19 $\dfrac{6}{x} - \dfrac{3}{2x} = 5$

20 $\dfrac{6}{x} + \dfrac{1}{x-5} = 2$

EXERCISE 27.3

Solve these simultaneous equations.

1 $y = x$
$y = x^2 - 20$

2 $y = x + 2$
$y = x^2 - 4$

3 $y = 4 - 5x$
$y = x^2 - 10$

4 $y = 7x + 4$
$y = 2x^2$

5 $x^2 = 3 + y$
$y = 6x - 11$

6 $y = 2x$
$y = x^2 - 15$

7 $y = 2 - x$
$x^2 + y^2 = 20$

8 $y = 2x - 5$
$x^2 + y^2 = 25$

9 $x = 2y + 1$
$x^2 + y^2 = 13$

10 $y + 2 = 2x$
$x^2 + y^2 = 25$

11 $x + y = 8$
$y = 10 - x^2$

12 $x + y = 10$
$x^2 + y^2 = 122$

13 $y = 5x$
$y = x^2 + 2x - 18$

14 $y = 2x^2 - 7$
$y = 2x + 5$

15 $y = 2x + 1$
$x^2 + y^2 = 13$

16 $y = 3 - x$
$x^2 + y^2 = 29$

EXERCISE 27.4

Make x the subject of these equations.

1 $xr - t = px$

2 $px + q = rx + 5$

3 $5(x + k) = 3xy$

4 Make c the subject of the equation: $y(x + c) = 2(x - c)$

5 Make t the subject of the equation: $\dfrac{5+t}{t-r} = w$

Make x the subject of these equations.

6 $2x + a = cx - d$

7 $\dfrac{a}{x} + 2 = c$

8 $\dfrac{xy-5}{x} = 1$

9 $y = \dfrac{2x+k}{x-2}$

10 Make e the subject of the equation: $\dfrac{d}{4} - \dfrac{e}{5} = 3$

EXERCISE 27.5

1 The graph shows the value of a motorbike at the end of each year.
The value of the motorbike y at time t is given by the relation:

$y = p \times q^t$

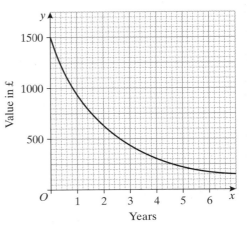

The curve passes through the point (0, 1500).
a) Use this information to show that $p = 1500$.
The curve also passes through (3, 444).
b) Use this information to find the value of q.
c) Work out the value of the motorbike after 4 years.

2 Ivan buys a car for £16 000.
Each year it falls in value by 40% of its value at the beginning of that year.
Ivan uses a mathematical equation to describe the value £V of his car y years after he bought it.
His equation is of the form $V = p \times q^y$, where p is a whole number and q is a decimal less than 1.
a) Write down the values of p and q.
b) Use Ivan's equation, with your values from part **a)**, to find the value of his car after 7 years.

3 Betty's Better Biscuit company employed 1200 people in 1992.
They had to reduce the number of workers by 8% per year for each year after 1992.
a) Write down the number of employees in
   (i) 1993   **(ii)** 1994.
   Write your answer to the nearest whole number.
b) The number of workers n years after 1992 is given by an expression of the form $p \times q^n$.
   Write down the values of p and q.
c) Hence find the number of employees in 2001.
   Write your answer to the nearest whole number.

4 Jasmine bought a new house.
Each year after that, its value increased by a fixed percentage of its value at the start of that year.
When the house was n years old its value was £130 000 $\times$ 1.04^n.
a) Write down how much Jasmine paid for the house.
b) Write down the percentage increase in value each year.
c) Work out the value of the house when it was 25 years old.
   Write your answer correct to the nearest £1000.

5 The number of ants, N, in a colony is given by the formula $N = 1600 + 850 \times 1.2^t$.
where t is the number of months after the total was first counted.
a) Find the number of ants in the colony when it was first counted.
b) Work out the number of ants in the colony 6 months after it was first counted.
c) Work out how many months it took after the first count for the colony to have over 10 000 ants.

U3 CHAPTER 28

Further trigonometry

EXERCISE 28.1

Find the lengths of the sides represented by letters.
Give your answers to 3 significant figures.

1

2

3

4

5

6

7

8

Find the angles represented by *x*. Give your answers to the nearest 0.1°.

9

10

11

12

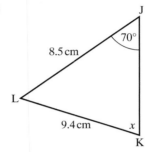

EXERCISE 28.2

Find the angles represented by letters. Give your answers to the nearest 0.1°.
If any are ambiguous, give both possibilities.

1

2

3

4

5

6

7

8

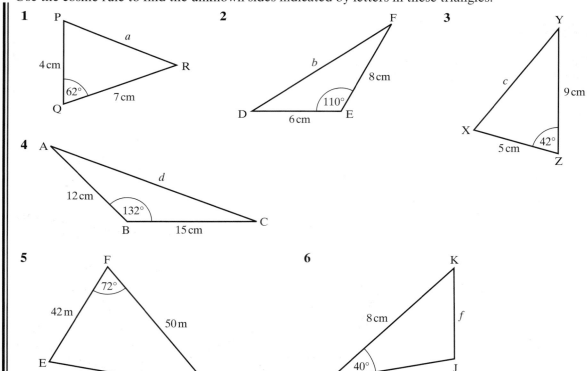

EXERCISE 28.3A

Use the cosine rule to find the unknown sides indicated by letters in these triangles.

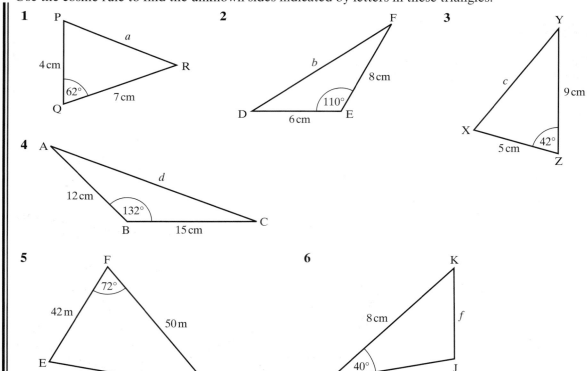

Use the cosine rule to find the unknown angles indicated by letters in these triangles.

7

8

9

10

 EXERCISE 28.3B

These are mixed questions on the sine and cosine rules.
Find the missing sides represented by letters.
Give your answers correct to 3 significant figures.

1

2

3

4

5

6

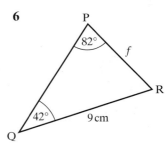

Find the unknown angles indicated by letters. Give your answers to the nearest 0.1°.

7

12 cm, 7cm, 24°, g, A, B, C

8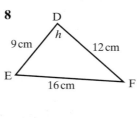

9 cm, 12 cm, 16 cm, D, E, F, h

9

15 cm, 6.24 cm, 132°, G, H, J, i

10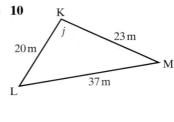

20 m, 23 m, 37 m, K, L, M, j

EXERCISE 28.4

1 In triangle PQR, RQ = 6.4 cm, angle PRQ = 43° and angle RPQ = 71°. Calculate:
 a) PR
 b) the area of triangle PQR.
  Give your answer correct to 3 significant figures.

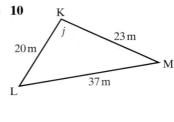

2 In triangle PQR, PQ = 13.7 cm, QR = 19.3 cm and PR = 12.1 cm.
 Calculate:
 a) the value of x
 b) the area of triangle PQR.
  Give your answer correct to 3 significant figures.

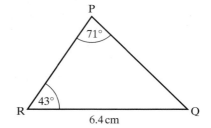

3 In triangle ABC, AB = 10 cm and BC = 5 cm.
 Angle ABC = 110°.
 a) Calculate AC.
  Give your answer correct to 3 significant figures.
 b) Calculate the size of angle BAC.
  Give your answer correct to the nearest 0.1°.
 c) Calculate the size of angle ACB.
  Give your answer correct to the nearest 0.1°.
 d) Calculate the area of triangle ABC.
  Give your answer correct to 3 significant figures.

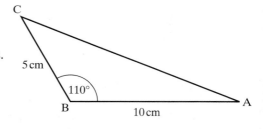

4 In triangle PQR, PQ = 5 cm, QR = 8 cm and RP = 12 cm.
 a) Calculate the size of angle PQR.
  Give your answer correct to the nearest 0.1°.
 b) Calculate the area of triangle PQR.
  Give your answer correct to 3 significant figures.

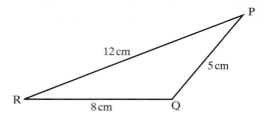

5 A chord PQ is drawn across a circle of radius 7 cm.
The chord PQ is of length 10 cm.
   a) Use the cosine rule to find angle POQ.
Give your answer to the nearest 0.1°.
   b) Hence find the area of the segment shaded in
the diagram.

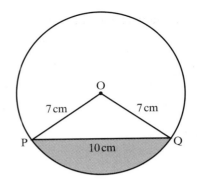

6 In triangle ABC, AB = 12 cm and AC = 10 cm.
The area of triangle ABC is 40 cm².
   a) Calculate the size of angle BAC.
Give your answer correct to the nearest 0.1°.
   b) Calculate the perimeter of triangle ABC.
Give your answer correct to 3 significant figures.

7 The diagram shows a regular pentagon inscribed inside a circle of radius 8 cm.

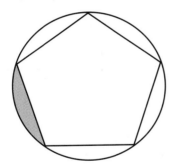

   a) Work out the area of the circle.
   b) Work out the area of the segment shaded on the diagram.
   c) Hence work out the area of the pentagon.
Give all your answers correct to 3 significant figures.

8 An isosceles triangle has sides of length 5 cm, 5 cm and 7 cm.
Work out the area of this triangle.

EXERCISE 28.5

1 The diagram shows a box in the shape of a cuboid ABCDEFGH.

   AB = 5 cm, BC = 4 cm, CG = 3 cm.

   A string runs diagonally across the box from A to G.
   a) Calculate the length of the string AG.
   Give your answer correct to 3 significant figures.
   b) Work out the angle between the string AG and the horizontal plane ABCD.
   Give your answer correct to the nearest 0.1°.

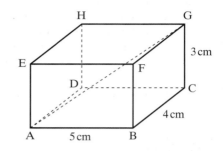

2 The diagram shows a square-based pyramid ABCDX.
   AB = BC = 8 cm.
   The point M is the centre of the square base ABCD.
   XM = 10 cm.
   a) Calculate the length of AC.
   Give your answer correct to 3 significant figures.
   b) Work out the angle between the edge AX and the horizontal plane ABCD.
   Give your answer correct to the nearest 0.1°.

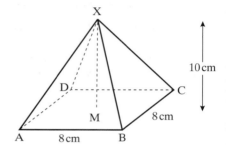

3 The diagram shows a wedge in the shape of a prism PQRSUV.

   PQ = 9 cm, QR = 18 cm, UR = 15 cm.

   String runs diagonally across the box from P to U.
   a) Calculate the angle UQR.
   Give your answer correct to the nearest 0.1°.
   b) Calculate the length PU.
   Give your answer correct to 3 significant figures.
   c) Work out the angle between PU and the horizontal plane PQRS.
   Give your answer correct to the nearest 0.1°.

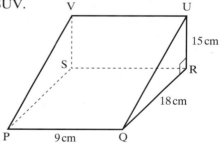

4 The diagram shows a cuboid ABCDEFGH.
   AB = 7 cm, BC = 10 cm, AG = 15 cm.
   a) Calculate the length AE.
   Give your answer correct to 3 significant figures.
   b) Work out the angle between CE and the horizontal plane ABCD.
   Give your answer correct to the nearest 0.1°.

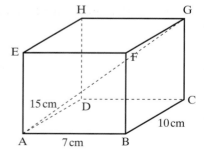

28 Further trigonometry U3

5 The cuboid PQRSJKLM has a square base PQRS.
PQ = QR = 12 cm, LR = 9 cm.
   a) Calculate the length QS.
         Give your answer correct to 3 significant figures.
   b) Calculate the length QM.
         Give your answer correct to 3 significant figures.
   c) Work out the angle between QM and the horizontal
         plane PQRS.
         Give your answer correct to the nearest 0.1°.

EXERCISE 28.6

1 A cone of height 12 cm has a base radius of 9 cm.
   a) Work out the volume of the cone.

   A smaller cone of height 5 cm is removed from the top of
   this cone to make a frustum.
   b) Work out the base radius of the smaller cone.
   c) Work out the volume of the frustum.

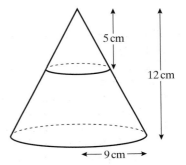

2 The diagram shows a cone of height 10 cm.
   The slant height of the cone, indicated on the diagram, is 14 cm.
   a) Work out the radius of the base of the cone.
   b) Hence work out the volume of the cone.

   The cone is cut by removing a smaller cone of height 5 cm,
   to leave a frustum.
   c) Work out the volume of the frustum.

3 Find the volume of this frustum of a cone.
   Give your answer correct to 3 significant figures.

U3 CHAPTER 29

Graphs of curves

 EXERCISE 29.1

1 Complete the table of values for the function $y = x^2 + 7$.
Two values have been filled in for you.

x	-3	-2	-1	0	1	2	3
y		11					16

2 Complete the table of values for the function $y = 3x^2 + x$.
Two values have been filled in for you.

x	-2	-1	0	1	2	3
y		2				30

3 Complete the table of values for the function $y = x - x^2$.
Two values have been filled in.

x	-2	-1	0	1	2	3
y		-2			-2	

4 Complete the table of values for the function $y = x^2 + 2x$.

x	-3	-2	-1	0	1	2
y						

5 Complete the table of values for the function $y = x^3 - 3$.

x	-2	-1	0	1	2	3
y						

6 Complete the table of values for the function $y = \dfrac{6}{x}$.

x	-3	-2	-1	0	1	2	3
y				not defined			

7 Complete the table of values for the function $y = 3^x$.

x	-2	-1	0	1	2	3
y						

8 Complete the table of values for the function $y = x + 2x^2$.

x	-2	-1	0	1	2	3	4
y							

EXERCISE 29.2

1 The table shows values of the function $y = x^2 - 2$ for $-3 \leqslant x \leqslant 3$.

x	-3	-2	-1	0	1	2	3
y	7	2	-1	-2	-1	2	7

a) Draw a set of coordinate axes on squared paper, so that x can range from -3 to 3 and y from -3 to 8, and plot these points on your axes.
b) Join your points with a smooth curve.
c) Use your graph to find the value of y when $x = 2.5$.
d) Find the coordinates of the lowest point on the curve.

2 The table shows some values of the function $y = 3x - x^2$.

x	-2	-1	0	1	2	3	4	5
y		-4			2			-10

a) Copy and complete the table.
b) Draw a set of coordinate axes on squared paper, so that x can run from -2 to 5 and y from -10 to 4. Plot these points on your graph, and join them with a smooth curve.
c) Give the coordinates of the highest point on the graph.

3 The table shows some values of the function $y = 3x^2 - 5$.

x	-3	-2	-1	0	1	2	3
y		7			-2		

a) Copy and complete the table.
b) Draw a set of coordinate axes on squared paper, so that x can run from -3 to 3 and y from -6 to 25. Plot these points on your graph, and join them with a smooth curve.
c) Use your graph to find all the solutions to the equation $3x^2 - 5 = 0$.

4 The table shows some values for the function $y = x^3 + 15$.

x	-3	-2	-1	0	1	2	3
y	-12				16		

a) Copy and complete the table.
b) Draw a set of coordinate axes on squared paper, so that x can run from -3 to 3 and y from -15 to 50. Plot these points on your graph, and join them with a smooth curve.

c) Use your graph to solve the equation $x^3 + 15 = 0$.
d) Use your graph to solve the equation $x^3 + 15 = 20$.

5 The table shows some values of the function $y = 2^x - 3$.

x	-2	-1	0	1	2	3	4
y	-2.75		-2				13

a) Copy and complete the table.
b) Draw a set of coordinate axes on squared paper, so that x can run from -2 to 4 and y from -3 to 14. Plot these points on your graph, and join them with a smooth curve.
c) Use your graph to solve the equation $2^x - 3 = 11$.

6 The table shows some values of the function $y = 2 - x^2$.

x	-3	-2	-1	0	1	2	3
y		-2		2			-7

a) Copy and complete the table.
b) Draw a set of coordinate axes on squared paper, so that x can run from -3 to 3 and y from -8 to 3. Plot these points on your graph, and join them with a smooth curve.
c) State the coordinates of the point on the curve where y takes its maximum value.
d) Use your graph to find the two solutions to the equation $2 - x^2 = 0$.

7 The table shows some values of the function $y = \dfrac{8}{x}$. The function is not defined when $x = 0$.

x	-8	-4	-2	-1	0	1	2	4	8
y			-4		not defined		4		

a) Copy and complete the table.
b) Draw a set of coordinate axes on squared paper, so that x can run from -8 to 8 and y from -8 to 8. Plot these points on your graph.
c) Join the first four points with a smooth curve.
d) Join the last four points with another smooth curve.
e) Use your graph to solve the equation $\dfrac{8}{x} = 5$.

8 The table shows some x values for the function $y = 2x^2 + x - 6$.

x	-3	-2	-1	0	1	2	3
y							

a) Copy and complete the table.
b) Draw a set of coordinate axes on squared paper, so that x can run from -3 to 3 and y from -7 to 16. Plot these points on your graph, and join them with a smooth curve.
c) Write down the solutions to the equation $2x^2 + x - 6 = 0$.
d) Give the coordinates of the minimum point on the curve.

9 The diagram shows part of the graph of the
function $y = x^2 - 4x + 2$.

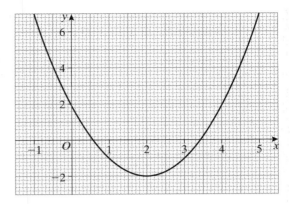

   a) Use the graph to find the two solutions
   to the equation $x^2 - 4x + 2 = 0$.
   b) Use the graph to find the two solutions
   to the equation $x^2 - 4x + 2 = 1$.

10 The diagram shows part of the graph of $y = 2 + \dfrac{1}{x}$.

   Use the graph to find a solution to the equation $2 + \dfrac{1}{x} = 4.5$.

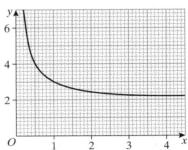

EXERCISE 29.3

1 Draw three sketch graphs to show
   a) $y = \sin x$ **b)** $y = \cos x$ **c)** $y = \tan x$
   for values of x between $-90°$ and $270°$.

2 Here are some statements about trigonometric functions. Decide whether each one is true or
   false. Try to deduce the answer from graphical considerations rather than using a calculator!
   a) $\sin 210°$ and $\sin 330°$ have the same value.
   b) $\cos 210°$ and $\cos 330°$ have the same value.
   c) $\sin x$ always lies between 0 and 1.
   d) $\tan x$ cannot be negative provided x lies between 0 and $180°$.
   e) $\tan 30°$ and $\tan 210°$ have the same value.

3 Here are some clues about trigonometric functions.
   For each one, decide whether it is referring to $y = \sin x$, $y = \cos x$ or $y = \tan x$.
   a) This function has a minimum when $x = 270°$.
   b) This function is not defined when $x = 270°$.
   c) The graph of this function passes through the point $(180°, 0)$.
   d) The graphs of these two functions have rotational symmetry order 2.
   e) This function has a minimum when $x = 180°$.

EXERCISE 29.4

1 The diagram shows part of
  the graph of $y = f(x)$.

  On a copy of the diagram,
  draw the graphs of:
  a) $y = f(x - 2)$
  b) $y = f(x) - 3$
  c) $y = 2f(x)$.
  Label your three graphs
  clearly.

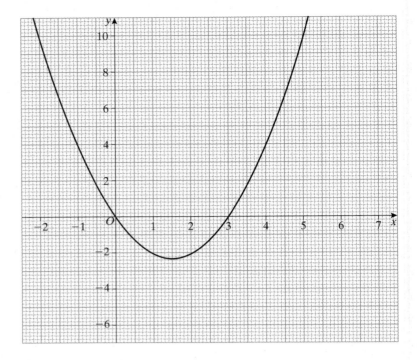

2 The diagram shows part of the graph of $y = f(x)$.

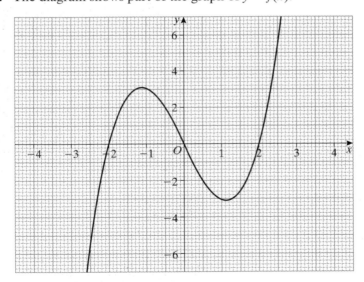

On a copy of the diagram, draw the graphs of:
a) $y = f(x + 1)$ **b)** $y = f(x) + 2$ **c)** $y = -f(x)$.
Label your three graphs clearly.

3 The diagram shows part of the graph of $y = f(x)$.

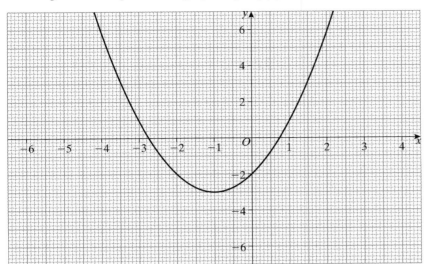

On a copy of the diagram, draw the graphs of:
a) $y = f(x - 2)$ **b)** $y = f(x - 2) - 3$ **c)** $y = -f(x)$.
Label your three graphs clearly.

4 The diagram shows
part of the graph of
$y = f(x)$.

On a copy of the
diagram, draw the
graphs of:
a) $y = f(-x)$
b) $y = -f(x)$
c) $y = f(x) + 2$.
Label your three
graphs clearly.

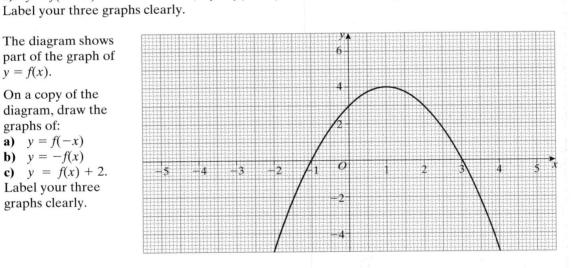

5 The diagram shows part of the graph of
$y = a\cos(x - b)$, where a and b are constants.

Work out the values of a and b.
Explain your reasoning.

6 The diagram shows part of the graphs of $y = f(x)$ and $y = f(x + a) + b$.

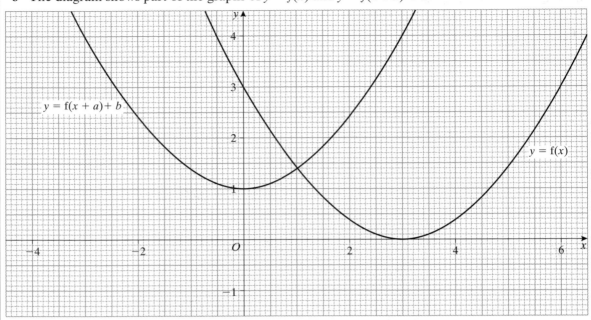

$y = f(x + a) + b$

$y = f(x)$

Work out the values of a and b. Explain your reasoning.

7 The diagram shows part of the graph of $y = a\sin (bx)$.

Work out the values of a and b.
Explain your reasoning.

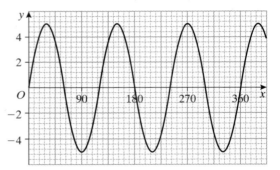

8 The diagram shows part of the graph of $y = a\sin x$.

Work out the value of a.
Explain your reasoning.

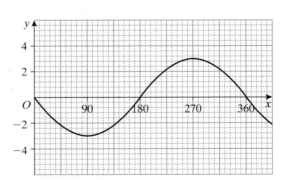

U3 CHAPTER 30

Vectors

EXERCISE 30.1

1 The diagram below shows some vectors drawn on a grid of unit squares.
   Write down column vectors to describe each one.

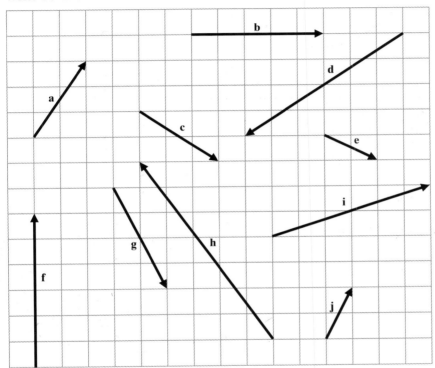

2 Draw a sketch of each of these vectors on squared paper.

a) $\begin{bmatrix} 4 \\ 2 \end{bmatrix}$ b) $\begin{bmatrix} -3 \\ 5 \end{bmatrix}$ c) $\begin{bmatrix} 6 \\ -1 \end{bmatrix}$ d) $\begin{bmatrix} -2 \\ -3 \end{bmatrix}$

EXERCISE 30.2

The vectors $\mathbf{p}$, $\mathbf{q}$ and $\mathbf{r}$ are given by $\mathbf{p} = \begin{bmatrix} 6 \\ 3 \end{bmatrix}$, $\mathbf{q} = \begin{bmatrix} -1 \\ -4 \end{bmatrix}$ and $\mathbf{r} = \begin{bmatrix} -5 \\ 2 \end{bmatrix}$.

Work out each of these as a column vector. Illustrate your answer with a diagram.

1 $\mathbf{p} + \mathbf{q}$ 2 $\mathbf{r} - \mathbf{p}$ 3 $\mathbf{q} + \mathbf{r}$ 4 $\mathbf{q} - \mathbf{p}$

Work out:

5 $\mathbf{p} - \mathbf{r} + \mathbf{q}$ **6** $\mathbf{r} - \mathbf{q} + \mathbf{p}$

The vectors $\mathbf{c}$, $\mathbf{d}$ and $\mathbf{e}$ are given by $\mathbf{c} = \begin{bmatrix} 7 \\ -3 \end{bmatrix}$, $\mathbf{d} = \begin{bmatrix} 4 \\ 5 \end{bmatrix}$ and $\mathbf{e} = \begin{bmatrix} -2 \\ 1 \end{bmatrix}$.

Work out each of these as a column vector. Illustrate your answer with a diagram.

7 $\mathbf{e} - \mathbf{d}$ **8** $\mathbf{c} + \mathbf{d}$ **9** $\mathbf{d} - \mathbf{c}$ **10** $\mathbf{c} + \mathbf{d} + \mathbf{e}$

Work out:

11 $\mathbf{c} - \mathbf{e}$ **12** $\mathbf{e} - \mathbf{d} - \mathbf{c}$

13 You are given that $\begin{bmatrix} 5 \\ 3 \end{bmatrix} + \begin{bmatrix} x \\ -1 \end{bmatrix} = \begin{bmatrix} 3 \\ 2 \end{bmatrix}$. Find the value of x.

14 You are given that $\begin{bmatrix} 4 \\ x \end{bmatrix} - \begin{bmatrix} y \\ -7 \end{bmatrix} = \begin{bmatrix} 7 \\ 9 \end{bmatrix}$. Find the values of x and y.

15 You are given that $\begin{bmatrix} -5 \\ -8 \end{bmatrix} + \begin{bmatrix} 8 \\ y \end{bmatrix} = \begin{bmatrix} x \\ 2 \end{bmatrix}$. Find the values of x and y.

EXERCISE 30.3

The vectors $\mathbf{x}$, $\mathbf{y}$ and $\mathbf{z}$ are given by $\mathbf{x} = \begin{bmatrix} 8 \\ 2 \end{bmatrix}$, $\mathbf{y} = \begin{bmatrix} -4 \\ -1 \end{bmatrix}$ and $\mathbf{z} = \begin{bmatrix} -5 \\ 7 \end{bmatrix}$.

Work out:

1 $2\mathbf{x}$ **2** $\mathbf{z} + 3\mathbf{y}$ **3** $2\mathbf{y} - \mathbf{z}$

4 $10\mathbf{x} - 5\mathbf{z}$ **5** $\mathbf{y} + 3\mathbf{x} - 2\mathbf{z}$ **6** $2\mathbf{x} - 3\mathbf{y} + \mathbf{z}$

The vectors $\mathbf{d}$, $\mathbf{e}$ and $\mathbf{f}$ are given by $\mathbf{d} = \begin{bmatrix} 6 \\ 0 \end{bmatrix}$, $\mathbf{e} = \begin{bmatrix} 3 \\ -5 \end{bmatrix}$ and $\mathbf{f} = \begin{bmatrix} -4 \\ 1 \end{bmatrix}$.

Work out:

7 $2\mathbf{d}$ **8** $-2\mathbf{e}$ **9** $3\mathbf{f} - \mathbf{d}$

10 $5\mathbf{d} - \mathbf{e} + 4\mathbf{f}$ **11** $8\mathbf{e} - 6\mathbf{f}$ **12** $4\mathbf{d} - 3\mathbf{f} + 2\mathbf{e}$

13 You are given that $4\begin{bmatrix} 3 \\ 9 \end{bmatrix} + 2\begin{bmatrix} x \\ -1 \end{bmatrix} = \begin{bmatrix} 22 \\ 34 \end{bmatrix}$. Find the value of x.

14 You are given that $3\begin{bmatrix} x \\ y \end{bmatrix} - 5\begin{bmatrix} 0 \\ -2 \end{bmatrix} = \begin{bmatrix} 12 \\ 16 \end{bmatrix}$. Find the values of x and y.

15 You are given that $6\begin{bmatrix} 5 \\ -2 \end{bmatrix} + 3\begin{bmatrix} 8 \\ x \end{bmatrix} = \begin{bmatrix} y \\ -21 \end{bmatrix}$. Find the values of x and y.

X EXERCISE 30.4

1 The diagram shows triangle RPQ. M is the midpoint of RQ.
   $\overrightarrow{RP} = 2\mathbf{a}$ and $\overrightarrow{PQ} = 2\mathbf{b}$.

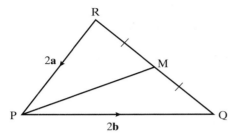

Find in terms of **a** and **b**, expressions for

a) $\overrightarrow{RQ}$ b) $\overrightarrow{RM}$

c) $\overrightarrow{PM}$ d) $\overrightarrow{MP}$

2 The diagram shows a parallelogram ABCD.
   AD is produced to E.
   $\overrightarrow{DE} = \mathbf{p}$ and $\overrightarrow{CE} = \mathbf{q}$. $DE = \frac{1}{3}AD$.

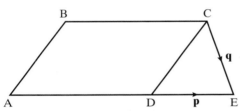

Find, in terms of **p** and **q**, expressions for:

a) $\overrightarrow{AD}$ b) $\overrightarrow{AB}$ c) $\overrightarrow{BD}$

d) What kind of quadrilateral is BCED?

3 A quadrilateral ABCD is made by joining the points A (0, 3), B (3, 1), C (5, 4) and D (2, 6).
   a) Write down column vectors for
       (i) $\overrightarrow{AB}$ (ii) $\overrightarrow{DC}$
   b) What do your answers tell you about AB and DC?
   c) Write down column vectors for
       (i) $\overrightarrow{BC}$ (ii) $\overrightarrow{AD}$
   d) What kind of quadrilateral is ABCD?

4 The diagram shows a quadrilateral ABCD. M is the midpoint of AC.

$\overrightarrow{AB} = 2\mathbf{p}$, $\overrightarrow{BM} = \mathbf{q}$ and $\overrightarrow{AD} = 3\mathbf{p} + 2\mathbf{q}$.

Find, in terms of $\mathbf{p}$ and $\mathbf{q}$, expressions for:

a) $\overrightarrow{AM}$ b) $\overrightarrow{AC}$

c) $\overrightarrow{CB}$ d) $\overrightarrow{DC}$

e) What kind of quadrilateral is ABCD?

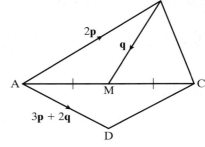

5 The diagram shows a parallelogram PQRS.

$\overrightarrow{PQ} = 2\mathbf{a}$ and $\overrightarrow{PS} = 2\mathbf{b}$.

L is the midpoint of PR.
M is the midpoint of QR.
Find, in terms of $\mathbf{a}$ and $\mathbf{b}$ expressions for:

a) $\overrightarrow{SR}$ b) $\overrightarrow{PR}$

c) $\overrightarrow{LM}$ d) $\overrightarrow{QM}$

e) Write down two facts about the relationship between LM and PQ.

6 A quadrilateral ABCD is made by joining A $(1, 3)$, B $(1, -5)$, C $(-2, -5)$ and D $(-2, 3)$.

a) Write column vectors for:

(i) $\overrightarrow{AB}$ (ii) $\overrightarrow{DC}$

b) What do your answers to part **a)** tell you about AB and DC?

c) Write column vectors for:

(i) $\overrightarrow{CB}$ (ii) $\overrightarrow{DA}$

d) What kind of quadrilateral is ABCD?

7 The diagram shows a kite ABCD. $\overrightarrow{AB} = 2\mathbf{a}$,

$\overrightarrow{AD} = 2\mathbf{b}$ and $\overrightarrow{CB} = 2\mathbf{c}$.
E, F, G and H are the midpoints of AB, BC, CD and DA respectively.

a) Explain why $\overrightarrow{DC} = 2\mathbf{a} - 2\mathbf{b} - 2\mathbf{c}$.

b) Find in terms of $\mathbf{a}$, $\mathbf{b}$ and $\mathbf{c}$:

(i) $\overrightarrow{EF}$ (ii) $\overrightarrow{HG}$

(iii) $\overrightarrow{EH}$ (iv) $\overrightarrow{FG}$

c) What can you deduce about the line segments EH and FG?

d) What type of quadrilateral is EFGH?

Mathematical proof

EXERCISE 31.1

1 Look at these pairs of triangles. In each case, decide whether the triangles are congruent or not.
   If they are congruent, explain why.

a)

b)

c)

d)

e)

f)

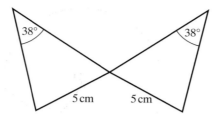

5 cm   5 cm

g)

8 cm

   39°

51°

8 cm

h)

50°   70°

4 m

60°

70°

4 m

2 The diagram shows two tangents, AB and AC, to a circle, centre O.

a) Show that the line segment OA bisects angle BOC.
[Hint: join OA and consider triangles AOB and AOC.]

b) Prove that OABC is a cyclic quadrilateral.

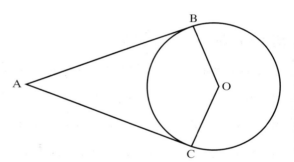

3 The diagram shows two triangles PQS and QRT.
Q bisects the line PR and QS = RT. QS is parallel to RT.

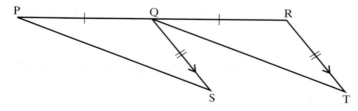

Prove that PS = QT.

4 The diagram shows a circle, centre O.
AB is a chord.
OM is perpendicular to AB.

Prove that M bisects AB.

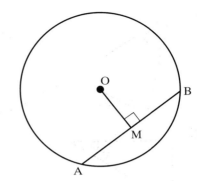

5 Q is the midpoint of the line segment PR and the line segment ST.

Prove that triangles PQS and RQT are congruent.

 EXERCISE 31.2

1 Prove that the sum of any two consecutive odd numbers is always a multiple of 4.

2 Prove that the sum of any five consecutive integers is always a multiple of 5.

3 Prove that the product of any two consecutive even numbers is always even.

4 Prove that the difference between any two consecutive integers is always 1.

5 Prove that the sum of the squares of any two consecutive numbers is always odd.

6 Look at this number pattern.
$$2^2 - 1^2 \;=\; 4 - 1 \;=\; 3 \;=\; 2 + 1$$
$$3^2 - 2^2 \;=\; 9 - 4 \;=\; 5 \;=\; 3 + 2$$
$$4^2 - 3^2 \;=\; 16 - 9 \;=\; 7 \;=\; 4 + 3$$
$$5^2 - 4^2 \;=\; 25 - 16 \;=\; 9 \;=\; 5 + 4$$
   a) Write down the next two lines in this number pattern.
   b) Show that the difference between the squares of any two consecutive numbers is equal to the sum of these two consecutive numbers by looking at:
      (i) $(n)^2 - (n-1)^2$ **(ii)** $x^2 - y^2$

7 a) Factorise $31^2 - 29^2$.   **b)** Hence show that $31^2 - 29^2 = 120$.

8 Show that the difference between the squares of any two consecutive even numbers is a multiple of 4.

EXERCISE 31.3

1 Anton says, 'The difference between any two prime numbers will always be a multiple of 2.'
    Show that Anton is wrong by giving two counter-examples.

2 Bob says, 'If a quadrilateral has two pairs of opposite sides equal in length then it must be a
    rectangle.' Show that this statement is false.

3 Carla says, 'If you multiply any two factors of 48 that are 8 or less, you will always get a factor
    of 48.' Show that Carla's statement is wrong.

4 Don says, 'You can find the lowest common denominator when adding two fractions less than
    one just by multiplying the two denominators together.'
    Show that this statement is false.

5 Evan says, 'If the four sides of a quadrilateral all have the same length, then the four internal
    angles must all be equal.'
    Draw a diagram to show that Evan is wrong.

6 The perfect squares are 1, 4, 9... which are numbers of the form n^2 where n is an integer.
    Integers to the power of 5 are 1, 32, 243... which are numbers of the form n^5 where n is an
    integer.
    David says, 'Apart from 1, there is no other number which is a perfect square and also a number
    of the form n^5.'
    Find a counter-example to show that David is wrong.

7 'If x is positive, then $4 + 4x - x^2$ is also positive.' Show that this statement is false.

8 Hans says, 'If you square a number the answer is always bigger than that number.'
    Show that Hans is wrong.

9 Ian says, 'If you have any quadrilateral that has the opposite sides equal in length, there will
    always be at least one line of reflection symmetry.'
    Draw a counter-example to show that Ian is wrong.

10 Joe says 'If n is a positive integer, then the value of $n^2 + n + 35$ is always prime.'
    Show that Joe is wrong.

U3 CHAPTER 32

Introducing coordinate geometry

EXERCISE 32.1

1 Use Pythagoras' theorem to calculate the distance from:
 a) A (6, 2) to B (3, 7)   **b)** P (−2, −7) to Q (3, 5)   **c)** M (−1, 4) to N (5, −1).

2 A triangle ABC has vertices A (−3, −1), B (1, 1) and C (−3, 4).
 Daisy makes a sketch of the triangle. Daisy says that the triangle is isosceles.
 a) Use Pythagoras' theorem to find the lengths of AB, AC and BC.
  You can give answers in surd form.
 b) Use your answers to decide whether Daisy is right or wrong.

3 A quadrilateral PQRS has vertices P (0, 1), Q (3, 2), R (5, 6) and S (2, 5).
 a) Make a rough sketch of the quadrilateral.
 b) Use Pythagoras' theorem to find the length of the sides PQ, QR, RS and SP.
  Give exact answers in surd form.
 c) What type of quadrilateral is PQRS?

4 Three points have coordinates A (1, 5, 3), B (6, 1, −5) and C (−2, −1, 4).
 Use the 3-D form of Pythagoras' theorem to find, as exact surds, the lengths of:
 a) AB   **b)** BC   **c)** CA.
 d) Which side of triangle ABC is the longest?

EXERCISE 32.2

1 A circle, centre O, has equation $x^2 + y^2 = 49$.
 Write down the radius of the circle.

2 A circle, centre O, has radius 8.
 Write down the equation of the circle.

3 A circle, centre O, has equation $x^2 + y^2 = 100$.
 Work out the diameter of the circle.

4 A circle, centre O, has diameter 12.
 Write down the equation of the circle.

5 A circle, centre O, passes through the point (3, 7).
 a) Work out the radius of the circle.
  Give your answer as a surd.
 b) Write down the equation of the circle.

6 A circle has equation $x^2 + y^2 = 169$.
 a) State the radius of the circle.
 b) Find the coordinates of the two
  points on the circle for which $y = 5$.

7 Find the coordinates of the two points where the graph of the line $y = x + 3$ meets the circle
 with equation $x^2 + y^2 = 29$.

8 A circle C is given by the equation $x^2 + y^2 = 50$.
 A line L is given by the equation $y = x + 10$.
 a) Prove that the line L cuts the circle C in exactly one place.
 b) Find the coordinates of this point.

9 Here are the equations of three graphs.
   Graph A $x = 30 + y$
   Graph B $x^2 = 30 + y$
   Graph C $x^2 = 30 - y^2$
   a) Which one of these is a circle?
   b) Describe the shapes of the other two graphs.

10 A circle C, with centre at the origin O, has diameter $\sqrt{200}$.
   a) Write this diameter in the form $10\sqrt{k}$, where k is an integer to be found.
   b) Hence find the equation of the circle C.

   A straight line has equation $y = x + 8$.
   c) Find the coordinates of the points where this line meets the circle C.

EXERCISE 32.3

1 For each of the following lines, write down:
   a) The gradient of a line parallel to the given line, and
   b) the gradient of a line perpendicular to the given line.

   (i) $y = 4x - 1$ **(ii)** $y = \dfrac{x}{3}$

   (iii) $y = 6 - 2x$ **(iv)** $2y = 9x - 4$

2 Find the equation of the straight line, parallel to $y = 2x + 7$, that passes through point P $(8, 6)$.

3 Find the equation of the straight line, parallel to $y = 3 - x$, that passes through point Q $(7, 2)$.

4 Find the equation of the straight line, perpendicular to $y = \frac{1}{2}x - 1$, that passes through the point P $(-2, -5)$.

5 Find the equation of the straight line, perpendicular to $y = 5x + 2$, that passes through the point Q $(5, 3)$.

6 Here are the equations of four straight lines.
   Line A $y = 15 - 8x$ **Line B** $y = 8x - 3$ **Line C** $y - 8x + 5 = 0$ **Line D** $y = \frac{1}{8}x + 3$
   a) Write down the names of the two lines that are **parallel**.
   b) Write down the names of the two lines that are **perpendicular**.

7 A line L passes through the points A $(0, 7)$ and B $(3, 5)$.
   a) Work out the gradient of the line L.   **b)** Work out the equation of the line L.
                                                           Give your answer in the form $y = mx + c$.

   A second line M is perpendicular to L. M passes through the point A.
   c) Write down the gradient of M.   **d)** Work out the equation of the line M.
                                                   Give your answer in the form $y = mx + c$.

8 Find the equation of the straight line, parallel to $y = 6 - 5x$, that passes through the point P $(1, 3)$.

9 Find the equation of the straight line, perpendicular to $y = 2 - x$, that passes through the point P $(-7, -4)$.

10 The lines $y = 8 - 3x$ and $y = ax + 2$ are perpendicular. Find the value of a.